G. M. Partridge

Editor:
    Michael A. Baughen
    assisted by Richard T. Bewes
Music Editor:
    David G. Wilson   Book 2

CONTENTS

INTRODUCTION AND ACKNOWLEDGEMENTS

THE EDITORS determined not to produce a second volume after *Youth Praise 1* unless it was clear that the Lord's hand was upon the preliminary exploration work for such a volume. As they looked at the hundreds of songs available, they found themselves enthusing over so many of them that they were left in no doubt that they should go ahead.

The vast majority of the contents of *Youth Praise 2* has never before been published, and none of it is to be found in our earlier book. There is a variation of style and quality similar to that of *Youth Praise 1*, to cater for the many different types of Youth groups that will use the book. It is the Editors' hope that groups will 'explore' the book thoroughly and not limit themselves to a small selection for regular use. There is much to 'find' here!

The way in which *Youth Praise 1* has been used has been beyond our wildest imaginations and we thank God for this. We 'launch' *Youth Praise 2* with the hope that it may be as much used as *Youth Praise 1* in giving expression to that 'new song' which is in the heart of every believer.

WE ACKNOWLEDGE with gratitude the help we have received from many people in the production of *Youth Praise 2*.

Our publishers have given every possible assistance and we owe much to the Rev. T. Dudley-Smith, the Rev. G. H. Reid and Miss J. Hewitt for all their interest, encouragement and labour and especially to Miss G. Woodward who has handled all the copyright and production details; also to Mrs R. V. Bazire for proof-reading the music; to Mrs A. Corbishley for much secretarial assistance; and to Mrs M. A. Baughen for help in many ways.

In the work of musical arrangement we particularly wish to thank the Rev. N. L. Warren, Mr M. C. T. Strover, Mr G. R. Timms, Mr J. D. Thornton and Mr O. J. Thomas. As with *Youth Praise 1* this book would not have been possible without the expert technical assistance of the Arnold Reproduction Company and encouragement from Mr F. W. Birkenshaw.

All items in this book are copyright, and the Editors and publishers gratefully acknowledge many kindnesses in permitting the inclusion of copyright material. Every effort has been made to trace copyright-holders, but any errors or omissions will gladly be put right at the first opportunity.

M. A. B.
D. G. W.
R. T. B.

A selection of songs from this book has been recorded on a long-playing record produced especially to mark the book's publication. Entitled *Tribute to Youth Praise* it has been produced by *Key Records* and is distributed by *The Scripture Union*.

Praise

151 Let us praise

Words and Music: **G. Brattle**

Let us praise, as we raise heart and voice to God a-bove

Let it ring, As we sing out the sto - ry of His love.

Let it flow, Let it grow, Let it rise from ev-'ry shore: Be ad-

-ored, Christ the Lord, Praise His Name for ev - er - more!

152 Let us praise God together

Words: J.E. Seddon
Music: Calhoun Melody
arr. D.G. Wilson

Let us praise God to-geth-er, Let us praise.

Let us praise God to-geth-er, Him pro-claim.

He is faith-ful in all His ways, He is worth-y of all our praise,

His name be ex-al-ted on high.

2. Let us seek God together,
   Let us pray,
   Let us seek His forgiveness
   As we pray.
   He will cleanse us from all sin,
   He will help us the fight to win,
   His Name be exalted on high.

3. Let us serve God together,
   Let us serve;
   Let our lives show His goodness
   As we work.
   Christ the Lord is the world's true light,
   Let us serve Him with all our might;
   His Name be exalted on high.

© J.E. Seddon and D.G. Wilson 1969. By kind permission.

153 Blessed be the Lord

Words: Psalm 68.19
Music: John van den Hogen

Bless-ed be the Lord_____ who dai- ly bears us up,_____

E   G#7 C# C#7   F#m

_ He takes our cares._____ Blessed be the Lord._____

B7   E

_ Ev - en the God._____ of our sal - va - tion. _

B+   Bm   C#   F#m

_____ Blessed be the Lord.   Blessed be the Lord._____

B7   E

154 I've got something to sing about

REFRAIN:

Words and Music: K. W. Wood

I've got something now to sing a - bout, and shout a - bout, and

G   C   D   C

tell a - round. I've got ev-'rything to sing a - bout, since

G   C   D

vv. 1, 2, & 4

Je-sus took my sins a -way. I know that Je - sus, He is my Sa -

C   G   B7

- - - viour; Oh, how He suffered for me. God's judg -ment

Em   B7   Em

poured on Him my Lord and He did it for me,— so that I could be free.

A7 D D7

v3

Right down in -to this

G F

sin - sick world,— from heav - en's glo - ry He came

E Am G F

To bleed and die on Cal - va-ry's cross to

E Am G C F

save us from sin and shame, He came.

✛ Coda

-way. Life for me is now so

won-der - ful, since Je-sus took my sins a - way.

2. I've got something now to sing about, and shout about, and tell around.
    Life for me is now so wonderful, since Jesus took my sins away.
    Each day now ev'rywhere that I go I know Jesus is there by my side.
    His life within helps me to win over anger and pride, 'cos He's living inside.

3. I've got ev'rything to sing about, and shout about, and tell around.
    Oh just let me tell to ev'ryone, how Jesus died and rose again.
    Right down into this sin-sick world, from heaven's glory He came.
    To bleed and die on Calvary's cross to save us from sin and shame, He came.

4. I've got ev'rything to sing about, and shout about, and tell around.
    Oh just let me tell to ev'ryone, how Jesus died and rose again.
    Each day now ev'rywhere that I go I know Jesus is there by my side.
    His life within helps me to win over anger and pride, 'cos He's living inside.

    I've got ev'rything to sing about, and shout about, and tell around.
    Life for me is now so wonderful, since Jesus took my sins away.
    Life for me is now so wonderful, since Jesus took my sins away.

155 There is joy

Words and Music: **M.J.H. Fox**

There is | joy, there is | joy, There is | joy be-fore the | an-gels ov - er

E   Emaj.7   E6   E

Ev - 'ry | per -son who re |-pents of | sin. There is | joy, there is

B7   E   A   E

joy   There is | joy   be-fore   the | an - gels ov - er | Ev - 'ry

E maj.7   E6   E   B7

sin - ner who re - | pents._____ | All the | heav- ens | ring As the

E   A

an-gels sing, And wor-ship our most glo-rious King.And they praise the

E   E6   B7   E   A

name Of the Lord who came To seek the blind and lost and lame.

E   E6   F#7   B7

© M.J.H. Fox 1969. By kind permission.

156 Lord of the years

Words: T.Dudley-Smith
Music: M.A. Baughen and D.G. Wilson

♩ = c.90
Unison

Lord,   for   the   years   your   love   has   kept   and

C   C6   C   F6   C

guid - - ed,   Urged   and   in - spired   us,

G7   C   C6   Am6   Em   D7

cheered us on____ our way, Sought____ us and

G   Am7   D7   G   C

saved us, par - doned and pro - vi - ded,

F   Dm   G7

Lord of the years, we bring our thanks to - day.

Am   Em   C   F   Dm   G7   C

2. Lord, for that Word, the Word of life which fires us,
   Speaks to our hearts and sets our souls ablaze.
   Teaches and trains, rebukes us and inspires us,
   Lord of the Word, receive your people's praise.

3. Lord, for our land, in this our generation,
   Spirits oppressed by pleasure, wealth and care;
   For young and old, for commonwealth and nation,
   Lord of our land, be pleased to hear our prayer.

4. Lord, for our world, when men disown and doubt Him,
   Loveless in strength and comfortless in pain;
   Hungry and helpless, lost indeed without Him,
   Lord of the world, we pray that Christ may reign.

5. Lord for ourselves; in living power remake us -
   Self on the cross and Christ upon the throne -
   Past put behind us, for the future take us,
   Lord of our lives, to live for Christ alone.

157 Sing praise

Words: Johann Jakob Schultz
tr. Frances Elizabeth Cox
Music: D. Phillips

Verse

Sing praise to God who reigns a-bove The God of all cre-a-tion, The God of pow'r, the God of love the God of our sal-va-tion; With healing balm my soul He fills,   And ev-'ry faith-less   murmur   stills:

C6   Am   D7   C   F#°   G

To God all praise and   glo - ry.

Em   Am   D7   G   C

Last verse only.

G   C   G   C   G

2. What God's almighty power hath made,
    His gracious mercy keepeth;
    By morning glow or evening shade
    His watchful eye ne'er sleepeth;
    Within the kingdom of His might,
    Lo! all is just and all is right:
    To God all praise and glory.

3. The Lord is never far away,
    But, through all grief distressing,
    An ever-present help and stay,
    Our peace, and joy, and blessing;
    As with a mother's tender hand,
    He leads His own, His chosen band:
    To God all praise and glory.

4. Thus, all my toilsome way along,
    I sing aloud Thy praises,
    That men may hear the grateful song
    My voice unwearied raises;
    By joyful in the Lord, my heart,
    Both soul and body bear your part:
    To God all praise and glory.

158 Be this my joy today

Words and Music: **G. Brattle**

Be this my joy to-day___ To hear and

to ob - ey My Sav -iour's word,___ His won-der-ful

word___ To read in ev - 'ry line God's will, and

make it mine___ Be this my joy___ my won-der-ful joy!___

159 In my heart

Words: (Dans Mon Cœur) C. Roda
Trans. M. Ponsford and M.A. Baughen
Music: C. Roda and J. Lacombe

REFRAIN:

In my heart there sings a

G   G7   C6

song, Song of all e - ter - ni -

G   D9

- ty In my

G   G6   G+   G

heart there sings a song

G7   C6   G

To verse

Of my Sa - viour's love to me._____

D9   G

To finish (last time)   *Fine*

me._____

G7   G

VERSES:

He   for   me   left be - hind   the Fa - ther's

C6   Em7   D7   G
                              Am

throne -   for   me,   just a   sin - ner   like

G   Am7   D7

me._____ And for me He was

left all a - lone - for me, yes dear

Lord, just for me.

2. He for me came to be crucified -
   For me, just a sinner like me.
   And for me came to suffer and die -
   For me, yes dear Lord, just for me.
   Chorus

3. He for me rose again from the grave -
   For me, just a sinner like me.
   And for me He will come back one day -
   For me, yes dear Lord, just for me.
   Chorus

Psalmody
160 Blessed is the man (Psalm 1)

Words arr: M.A.Baughen
Music: M.A. Baughen
arr: J.D. Thornton

man. But his de - light by day and

F C7 F Gm7 C7 F

For last two lines D.S.al Fine

night Is the law of God Al - migh - ty.

Gm7 C7 F7 B♭ Gm F C7 F

2. He is like a tree - a tree that flourishes
   Being planted by the water - blessed is that man.
   He will bring forth fruit - his leaf will wither not -
   For in all he does he prospers - blessed is that man.
   For his delight - by day and night -
   Is the law of God Almighty.

3. The wicked are not so - for they are like the chaff -
   Which the wind blows clean away - the wicked are not so.
   The wicked will not stand - on the judgment day -
   Nor belong to God's people - the wicked will not stand.
   But God knows the way of righteous men
   And ungodly ways will perish.

   Blessed is the man, the man who does not walk
   In the counsel of the wicked - blessed is that man.

VERSION B   *Music:* M.A. Baughen and D.G. Wilson

Bless - ed is the man___ the man who does not___
He who re-jects the way___ re jects the way of

F C7 F Gm7 C7

161 Why do the heathen (Psalm 2)

Words arr: M.A.Baughen
Music: M.A. Baughen and J.D. Thornton

Why do the heathen con - spire?

Peoples are plotting in vain, Kings of the earth de -

-clare A-gainst God and His An - nointed One:

Break all their bonds a - sun - der,

Let   us   be   done_____   with   their   cords.

G   Em   Am7   D7   G

2. He who is sitting in heaven
    Laughs them to scorn, as the Lord,
    He will address them in wrath
    And they fear as they listen to His words:
    'I have set up my true King,
    He is on my holy hill. '

3. This is the word from the Lord -
    He told me, 'You are my son:
    Ask of me and I will make
    All the nations of earth your heritage.
    You shall bruise them with iron
    Dash them in pieces like a vase'.

4. Now therefore, kings of the earth,
    Think and take warning from this.
    Yield to the Lord and serve Him
    Kneeling down before Him in reverence.
    Do not ignore and perish
    Blessed are all those who trust in Him.

162 O Lord our God (Psalm 8)

Words and Music: M.A.Baughen
arr: J.D. Thornton

O   Lord,   our   God!   How ma -jes-tic is   your

C7   F   Am   Dm   Gm7

name   in   all   the   earth!   1.Your glo - ry is tran -

To Coda⊕ (5th time)
Verse

C7   F   Bb   C6

-cen - dent Yet chil - dren sing your praise Your

F   Dm   Gm7   F   Bb   C7

en - em - ies are si - lenced Be - fore your ma - jes - ty.

F   Dm   Am   G7   C7

⊕ Coda

O Lord, Our God! How ma-jes-tic is your name in all the earth!

F7 Bb D7   Gm   A7 Dm Gm7 C7   F

2. I stand to view the heavens
Created by your hands
You placed the moon and stars there
And yet you care for man.
O Lord, our God!
How majestic is your name in all the earth!

3. To man you gave such honour
You made him almost god
In giving him dominion
Over created things.
O Lord, our God!
How majestic is your name in all the earth!

4. You put beneath man's ruling
All animals of earth
The birds that fly above him
And all within the sea.

O Lord, our God!
How majestic is your name in all the earth!
O Lord, our God!
How majestic is your name in all the earth!

163 O Lord our Lord(Psalm 8)

Words: E.Bash
Music: Traditional
arr. D.G. Wilson

2. When I think on Thy heavens, the work of Thy fingers,
    The moon and the stars which Thou hast ordained
    What is man in Thy mem'ry, a man that Thou mindest
    The son of man that Thou carest for him.

3. Thou hast made him just lower than angels of glory,
    And crowned him with honour and glory and power.
    Thou gavest dominion o'er all of the wide earth,
    And all of the creatures that run in the sea.

164 The Lord is my Shepherd (Psalm 23)

Words: J.E. Seddon
Music: N.L. Warren

1. The | Lord is my Shepherd, I | nev - er shall want; He

makes me in pas - tures to | lie;_____ Be-| side the still wa - ters He

gent - ly will lead My___ | needs He will dai - ly sup | -ply._____

2. The Lord is my Saviour, my soul He restores,
   He found me when lost and astray;
   He shows me the way of His Truth and His will
   And helps me to trust and obey.

3. The Lord is my shield, I no evil shall fear;
   He lightens the dark paths I tread;
   He always is with me, my rod and my staff,
   And now death itself has no dread.

4. The Lord is my strength, at His table I find
   The pow'r to defeat all my foes;
   My life He sustains with His kindness and power
   With blessing my cup overflows.

5. The Lord is my song, of His grace I will sing,
   I'll dwell in His house all my days;
   His goodness and mercy will follow me still,
   His Name I for ever will praise.

165 The earth is the Lord's (Psalm 24)

Words arr: M.A. Baughen
Music: M.A. Baughen and D.G. Wilson

The earth is the Lord's and the ful - ness there -of, The
world and the peo - ple there-in.
He has found-ed it up - on the seas, On
ri - ver floods He es - tab - lished all things.

2. So who shall ascend on the hill of the Lord?
   Or stand in the holiest place?
   He whose hands are clean and heart is pure
   Who is not false and is not deceitful.

3. And he will receive all the blessing of God
   His Saviour will vindicate him
   Such is everyone who seeks the Lord
   Who seeks the face of the God of Jacob.

4. Now lift up your heads O you gates and you doors
   The King of all Glory comes in!
   Who then is this King of Glory - who?
   The Lord Himself who is strong and mighty.

5. Now lift up your heads O you gates and you doors
   The King of all Glory comes in!
   Who then is this King of Glory - who?
   The Lord of Hosts is the King of Glory!

166 The Lord is my light (Psalm 27)

Words arr: **M.A. Baughen**
Music: **A. Plank**
arr. **D.G. Wilson**

Lord! 2.One see all Your good - ness, O Lord!

2. One thing which I seek is to live in God's house
   To gaze on His beauty and learn more of Him
   In trouble He will protect me
   Lifting my head
   And I will rejoice and will sing to the Lord'.

3. O Lord hear my voice when I call upon You,
   You said 'Seek my face' and Your face do I seek.
   In anger do not reject me
   You are my help
   I know I will see all Your goodness, O Lord!

© M.A. Baughen and A. Plank 1969. By kind permission.

167 I waited patiently (Psalm 40)

Words arr: M.A. Baughen
Music: M.A. Baughen and D.G. Wilson

1. I wait - ed pat - ient-ly for the Lord He turned and

lis - tened to me___ He drew me out of the

ech - o-ing pit And out of the mi - ry clay.____ He

set my feet up - on a rock My foot - steps

He made se - cure____ With - in my mouth He

put a new song A song of praise to God____

2. In many seeing it, fear will come -
They then will turn to the Lord
And he is happy who trusts in the Lord
Who will not be led astray.
Your wondrous deeds and thoughts to us
Are multiplied, O my God -
They number more than we can proclaim
Lord! None compares with You!

3. It is not offerings You require
But open ears to Your word
And so instead of a sacrifice
I come to You with my life.
I love to do Your will, my God,
Within my heart is Your law;
Deliverance is news I have told -
My lips have not been sealed.

4. I have not hidden within my heart
Your steadfast love and Your help -
The congregation have heard me declare
Salvation and faithfulness.
And so when evils circle me
Have mercy on me, O Lord
May all who love You thankfully say:
The Lord is great indeed!

168 Have mercy Lord (Psalm 51)

Words: J.M. Barnes
Music: D.G. Wilson

2. In judgment, Your word is blameless,
    For I have sinned since my beginning,
    And Lord, You long for truth in my life,
    So give me wisdom today.

3. Lord, wash me from my uncleanness,
    Fill me with joy where once was sadness,
    Give me a heart renewed, O my Lord,
    A new right spirit within.

4. Turn from my sins and destroy them,
    But let me never be forsaken.
    O give me joy in knowing You save,
    And make me love Your command.

5. I'll tell all those who ignore You
    And sinners then will come repentant.
    Lord, save me from the death I deserve
    Then I will tell what You've done.

6. Lord take my lips and I'll praise You;
    No sacrifice I bring redeems me.
    All that You want is my broken heart;
    A gift You will not refuse.

7. Lord give Your peace to Your servant.
    Protect and stay by me for ever.
    Through Your great love accept what I give
    And fill my life with Your praise.

169 If the building (Psalm 127)

Words and Music: D.G. Wilson

will not · end.___ 2. You're end.___

Bb6   C7   F   Bb   F   C7   F   Bb   F

2. You're careful to wake with the dawn.
   For your wages you toil till the evening.
   But the Lord gives the ones that He loves
   All His gifts even while they are sleeping.
   Chorus

3. Every child is a gift of the Lord,
   Those we love a great joy and a blessing,
   It is great to be blessed of the Lord,
   It's the life with which no-one can quarrel.
   Chorus

© D.G. Wilson 1969. By kind permission.

170 Faithful vigil ended
(Nunc Dimittus)

Words: T. Dudley-Smith
Music: D.G. Wilson

1. Faith-ful vi-gil end-ed, Watching, wait-ing cease;
2. All Thy spir-it prom-ised, All the Fa-ther willed,

Mas-ter, grant Thy ser-vant His dis-charge in peace.___
Now these eyes be-hold it Per-fect-ly ful-filled.___

3. This Thy great deliverance
   Sets Thy people free;
   Christ their light uplifted
   All the nations see.

4. Christ, Thy people's glory!
   Watching, doubting cease;
   Grant to us Thy servants
   Our discharge in peace.

© T. Dudley-Smith and D.G. Wilson 1969. By kind permission.

171 Gloria in Excelsis

Words arr: C. J. Laslett
Music: M.A. Baughen
arr. N.L. Warren

Glo-ry give to God in hea-ven; In the high - est, glo - ry be!

And on earth there's tru - est peace for men with whom the Fa-ther's pleased

So we praise you wor - ship, bless you Thank you for your love so great.

Heav'n - ly King Al - might - y Fa-ther, Lord and God we praise your name.

2. Lamb of God in triumph seated,
Jesus Christ our great high priest,
By your all-sufficient offering
You have cancelled all our sins.
  So through you we come with boldness,
  Fearless, to the Father's throne.
  Justified by faith, rejoicing,
  Lord and God we praise your name!

3. Holy Spirit, Lord, proceeding
From the Father and the Son,
You're the seal of our salvation.
Live and reign within our hearts.
  Father, Son and Holy Spirit,
  You alone are God Most High.
  Maker, Saviour, Sanctifier,
  Lord and God we praise your name!

alternative to verse 2

Lamb of God, Messiah, Jesus
God the Father's only Son,
Pity us, have mercy on us
You who take away our sins.
  You remove the world's offences,
  Hear us Lord. Receive our prayer.
  Pity us, have mercy on us,
  You who sits at God's right hand.

C

God
172 I know

Words and Music: The Crossbeats
arr: J. and B. Courtie

1. When I — see the sun-shine,— When I see the rain,
2. When I — see a lit- tle child, When it o - pens eyes,

Eb   Cm   Db   Bb7

When I see the things that grow, That feeling comes a - gain, And I
When I see that smil - ing face, and ev-en when it cries, I —

Eb   Cm   Fm   Bb7

know, yes I know, When I see these things I know That there's a
know, yes I know, When I see a child I know That there's a

Ab   Eb   Ab   F7

God of love and He made these things I know.
God of love and He made us all I

Eb   Cm   Fm   Bb7   Eb   B7   Bb7

know. When I'm feel-ing lone-ly and

Eb Ab Eb Bb7 Cm G7

blue_____ O I know God is wait-ing, and I

Cm F7

know He'll pull me through. I know that He can do it, be-cause He

Bb Bb+ Eb G7

did it once be - fore, When I first came to Je - sus, And I

Cm Eb7 Ab Bb7

know,   I   know   He's   mine   for ev-er - more.O   yes I

Eb   Fm7   Eb   Ab   Eb   Ab

know,   I   know   He's   mine   for ev-er - more.

Eb   Fm7   Eb   Ab   Eb

173 High over the world

Words and Music: Betty Lou Mills

Rhythmically

C   Ab7   C   Ab7   C   Ab7   C

God   cre - a - ted   the hea-ven and   earth,   God   cre -

C   C7   F7

world.

Last verse.

world.

2. God created the seasons,
   God created the stars:
   God created the fish and the fowl
   God created the cattle and beasts -
   He is high ...

3. God created man and woman
   In His image from the dust:
   And His power is yet the same
   If in Him we'll put our trust -
   He is high...

174 They say He's wonderful

Words: H. Pollock
arr: D. Delarue

1. He makes the rain to fall
    He sees the wheat grow tall
    The root, the shoot and soon the fruit,
    The root, the shoot and soon the fruit,
    It shows He cares for all.
    Chorus

2. When I see babies small,
    And I hear children call,
    And think of family life and fun,
    And think of family life and fun,
    I know He's behind it all
    Chorus

3. The love men have for Him
    Such love death cannot dim,
    Of small and great of rich and poor,
    Of small and great of rich and poor,
    Love like this comes from Him.
    Chorus

4. And I know He's wonderful,
    I know He's wonderful,
    The Son of God who died for me,
    The Son of God who died for me,
    I know He's wonderful.
    Chorus

175 God is there

Words: A.H. Zoller and F. Rauch
tr. S. Lonsdale and M.A. Baughen
Music: A.H. Zoller

Je -sus   we're   His!_____   God is   And   in

G7   C7   F

Je - sus   we're   His!_____

G7   C7   F7   C7

F

2. Satan offers his own happiness
    And we're tempted to turn from the Lord
    Yet we know that such happiness fades
    Without God we are helpless and poor.
    Chorus

3. Men make wars in this sin-ridden world
    Men have hearts in which selfishness reigns
    Men so often refuse to forgive
    Yet God loves us in spite of it all.
    Chorus

4. God was there when the world first began
    He'll be there when it passes away
    Everything is dependent on Him
    God is there just wherever we are
    Chorus

176 I love the flowers

Words and Music: G. McClelland
arr. P. Bye

See a cou-ple— hand in hand,— walk-ing bare-foot thro' the sand, A lov-ing girl and a lov-ing man But they don't love as much as God, Be - cause

Coda

You can live for ever - more you can live for ev-er - more.

177 Lord you sometimes speak in wonders

Words: C. Idle
Music: N.L. Warren

Lord, you sometimes speak in wonders Un - mis-tak-a - ble and clear;

F   Fmaj7 Dm7   Gm   C7   F   Fmaj7   Dm7   Gm Gm7   C7

Might-y—— signs to prove your prescence, Ov - er-coming doubt and fear

F   F7   Bb6 Bbm6   F   Am Dm6   G7   Am D7 Gsus.4 Gm   C7   F

2. Lord, you sometimes speak in whispers,
   Still and small and scarcely heard;
   Only those who want to listen
   Catch the all-important word.

3. Lord, you sometimes speak in silence,
   Through our loud and noisy day:
   We can know and trust you better
   When we quietly wait and pray.

4. Lord, you often speak in Scripture -
   Words that summon from the page,
   Shown and taught us by your Spirit
   With fresh light for every age.

5. Lord, you always speak in Jesus,
   Always new yet still the same;
   Teach us now more of our Saviour;
   Make our lives display His Name.

178 Our Father

Words: T. Dudley-Smith
Music: M.A. Baughen
arr. D.G. Wilson

Fa - ther who formed the fa-mi-ly of man, ___ High throned in hea-ven ev-er-more the same Our prayer is still as Christian prayer began, That hallowed be your Name. -more.

2. Lord of all Lords, the only King of kings,
Before whose countenance all speech is dumb,
Hear the one song the new creation sings -
Your promised kingdom come!

3. Father of mercy, righteousness and love,
Shown in the sending of that only Son,
We ask on earth, as in the realms above,
Your perfect will be done!

4. Lord of the harvest and the living seed,
The Father's gift from which the world is fed,
To us your children grant for every need
This day our daily bread.

5. Father, whose Son ascended now in heaven
Gave once Himself upon a cross to win
Man's whole salvation, as we have forgiven,
Forgive us all our sin.

6. Lord of all might and majesty and power,
Our true Deliverer and our great Reward,
From every evil, and the tempter's hour,
Deliver us, good Lord.

7. Father who formed the family of man,
Yours is the glory heaven and earth adore,
The kingdom and the power, since time began,
Now and for evermore.

179 If God desires it

Words: E. Vargas
Trans. S. Lonsdale and **M.A. Baughen**
Music: E. Vargas
arr. A.H. Zoller

If God de-sires it, all the flow'rs on earth____ will be

red,____ If God de-sires it all the stones will

turn____ in-to bread,____ If God all-ows it

we can play With moon and stars and milk - y way Or

And re - live our lives a - gain for
Bb7   Am7

bet - ter or for worse! Yet if we real - ly
G7   C   F

could   Would it be for our good   Much
C9   G7   C6

bet - ter that our ways be - long to
G7   C6

Him who un-der-stands   Much bet-ter that our

dest-i-ny   is   safe-ly   in   His hands

G   C   F7

Em7   G7   C   *D.C. al Fine*

180 The hills in their beauty

Words and Music: D. Kennedy
arr. D.G. Wilson

The hills in their beau-ty His splendour have shown The riv-ers in

G   G7   C   G   Em

tor - rent His greatness made known. Yet from all these won-ders God

chose man a - lone To be with Him each day.

But man in his blind-ness has gone a - stray For-sa-ken God's

law, des - pis - ing God's way. But all was for - giv-en that

glor - i - ous day When He died for me.

181 Beyond the grasp

Words: **M. Saward**
Music: **M.A. Baughen and D.G. Wilson**

Be - yond the grasp of hu - man brain, Great
God, ma - jest - ic Ru - ler, We
men by faith, Your pre - sence find In
Christ, our ris - en Mas - ter, And___

all the pow'r which we can use Though tur - bine, jet and

G   Em7   Am   D7   G   Am7 G

mo - tor Is___ no - thing to the

A7   D   G   C   Am   D7   Bm

pow'r of___ Christ Who frees us from dis - as - ter.

Em   Am   D   D7   G   C   Am7   D7   G

2. For me believe, despite the power
    Of greed and lust and Satan
    Which dominates the will of men,
    That sin can be forgiven.
    In humble trust and confidence
    No power our souls can frighten
    We spread your liberating truth
    That speaks of love in heaven.

3. Yet here, within your universe.
    We struggle with the Tempter
    He has no right to trick and trap,
    No right to make us cower.
    So, Spirit of the living Christ,
    The Saviour and the Victor,
    That we may daily overcome
    Uphold us with your power.

182 Who holds the keys?

Words: D. Green (Based on Revelation 1.17-18)
Music: R.T. Bewes
arr. M.C.T. Strover

The fu - ture now is dark, the path un - known; God's

peo - ple walk in night and seem a - lone. When

will the promised time come, and it all be shown -

God in con - trol - God on the throne?

2. Though nations rise and fall and kingdoms sway.
   Though wars and tumults rage day after day;
   His promise stands though heaven and earth may pass away;
   His word remains - true for today.

3. How much we need His Word in hours like these!
   More powerful than the threats of enemies:
   Above the raging of the storms and mighty seas -
   He is the Lord, He holds the keys.

4. Of life and death and hell, and every throne,
   He only holds the keys and He alone;
   Of heaven and glory and of all eternities,
   He is the Lord - He holds the keys.

183 God is all-loving

German Words and Music: A. Rische

God is all— lov - ing He has re - deemed me,

God is all lov - ing, and He loves me.

Chorus

And so I sing a - gain, God is all— lov - ing

God is all— lov - ing, and He loves me.

2. I lay in bondage to sin's dominion
   And as I lay I could not get free.
   Chorus

3. I lay within the death-grip of Satan
   Sin pays its servants wages of death.
   Chorus

4. But he sent Jesus, to be our Saviour
   But He sent Jesus, who set me free.
   Chorus

5. By pledge of pardon He loosed my burden
   His Holy Spirit lifted my load.
   Chorus

6. Your love is patient with my shortcomings
   Your love upholds me in all my need.
   Chorus

7. Your joy refreshes my fainting spirit
   Your peace envelopes my troubled heart.
   Chorus

8. Now I inherit eternal riches
   Through You inherit eternal rest.
   Chorus

9. O love eternal, I'll ever praise You
   For ever more Your love I'll proclaim.
   Chorus

Jesus
184 From Bethlehem to Calvary

Words and Music: Charles Rhoda
Trans. Mike Ponsford (adapted)
arr. John van den Hogan and D.G. Wilson

From Beth - le-hem to Cal - va - ry From the crib to the

cru - el tree, From des-pair to joy for me,

There is on - ly Je - sus. Oh Je - sus your love is so

great to me that it reach-es the depths of my heart. Oh

Je - sus, Your love, all your love for me, Makes my fear and my sor-row de -

D   Em7   D   D7   G   Am7   G   Bm   E7   A7

-part.   I   want ev - 'ry - one to know

D   G   D

Of   the   one   who loves me so___   Christ   a- lone can

Em7   A7   D   D7   G

D.S. al Fine

set   them free   And   Him they'll praise with   me.   From

D   F#m   A   E7   A7

185 Christ is the Lord

Words: K. Preston
Music: D. Brace and D. Baggs

all;___ Christ is the Lord of the hu -man heart beat,

Christ is the Lord of ev -'ry breath, Christ is the Lord of a

man's ex - is - tence, Christ is the Lord of life and death.

2. Christ is the Lord of our thoughts and feelings,
   Christ is the Lord of all we plan,
   Christ is the Lord of a man's decision,
   Christ is the Lord of total man;
     In the local street,
     Where the people meet,
     In the church or the nearby hall;
     In the factory,
     In the family,
     Christ is the Lord of all;
   Christ is the Lord of our love and courtship,
   Christ is the Lord of man and wife,
   Christ is the Lord of the things we care for,
   Christ is the Lord of all our life.

186 Only Jesus

Moderato

Words and Music: Betty Lou Mills

Who took fish and bread hun - gry people fed? Who changed wa - ter in - to wine? Who made well the sick, who made see the blind? Who touched earth with feet di - vine? On - ly Je - sus, On - ly Je - sus,

On - ly He has done this: Who made live the dead?
Truth and kindness spread? On - ly Je - sus did all this.
this.

2. Who walked dusty road? Cared for young and old?
   Who sat children on His knee?
   Who spoke words so wise? Filled men with surprise,
   Who gave all, but charged no fee?
   Only Jesus, Only Jesus, Only He has done this:
   Who in death and grief spoke peace to a thief?
   Only Jesus did all this.

3. Who soared through the air? Joined His Father there?
   He has you and me in view:
   He, who this has done, is God's only Son,
   And he's int'rested in you.
   Only Jesus, Only Jesus, Only He has done this:
   He can change a heart, give a new fresh start,
   Only He can do this.

187 I've tried in vain

Words: Verses 1 and 2, J. Proctor
Verses 3 and 4, R.J. Mayor
Music: R.J. Mayor

- gether for good with those who love and serve the Lord: I'll trust in Him for all I need For ev - er - more in Je - sus. In times like these, It can be hard to lift the cross and fol - low my Lord But He is with us. day by day, This ne - ver fail - ing Je - sus.

E

188 Through all our days

Words: M. Saward
Music: Traditional
arr. D.G. Wilson

Through all our days we'll sing the praise of Christ, the re - sur-rec - ted, Who, though di - vine,____ did not de - cline____ To be____ by men____ af - flic - ted. Pain, Pain,____ and suf - fer - ing,____ He knew its taste____ He bore its sting;

Peace, peace, to men on earth, Through Christ our King, and Sa - viour.

G   D   Em   B7   Em

2. His birth obscure, His family poor,
   He owned no crown, no kingdom.
   Yet men who grope in darkness, hope
   Since He brought light and freedom.
   Shame, Shame, and agony
   Though guiltless He of felony;
   Shout, Shout, His sinless name,
   Our Jesus, King and Saviour!

3. At fearful cost His life he lost
   That death might be defeated.
   The Man of Love, now risen above
   In majesty is seated.
   Low, Low, was His descent
   To men by sin and sorrow bent;
   Life, Life, to all who trust
   The Lord, our King and Saviour!

4. And all who trust will find they must
   Obey the will of heaven,
   For grief intense can make some sense
   To men who've been forgiven.
   Hard, Hard, the road He trod
   The Son of Man, the Son of God;
   Hope, Hope, in Christ alone,
   Our reigning King and Saviour!

© M. Saward and D.G. Wilson, 1969. By kind permission.

189 O Let us sing

CHORUS:

Words and Music: L.C. Taylor

O, let us sing of our mer - ci - ful King,

G   G7   C

Migh- ty Re-deem-er is He;— We give Him praise for His

G   A7   D7   G7

2. If you are weary and crushed with despair,
When Satan's power is strong,
Call to the One whom the foe must shun,
He'll give you strength and a song!
    Chorus

3. He breaks the fetters of sorrow and sin,
Raising men out of their plight,
He calms the waves on the stormy sea,
He turns the darkness to light.
    Chorus

4. He turns the wilderness into a well,
The barren land into a plain,
He makes the trusting and humble rejoice,
Giving them gladness again.
    Chorus

190 Wonderful Jesus

Words: J.B. Foote
Music: G. Bailey

2. Christ Jesus, Saviour and God, ruling on high,
Lonely the pathway you trod, destined to die,
Bearing our load of pain,
Now gone above to reign,
Glorious Son of God, Victor on high.

3. We praise you Jesus our Lord, Saviour and Friend,
For you our thanks we record. Joy without end.
Salvation's free reward,
Pardon and peace restored,
All from the Cross outpoured, wonderful Friend.

191 Christ the Light

Words: C. Idle
Music: N.L. Warren

Christ the Light who shines un-fad-ing In the sad, sin darkened mind Guid-ing those who grope in er-ror Op-'ning eyes that sin made blind; Shows himself the Lord of Glo-ry shin-ing for a lost man-kind.

D7 G6 D Bm D G6

2. Christ the Bread who came from Heaven
   Hungry souls to satisfy:
   Just as loaves must first be broken;
   Our Life-giver had to die;
     Made Himself a generous Offering,
     Gave Himself for our supply.

3. Christ the Life who rose in splendour
   From the cold and dismal cave.
   On the Resurrection-morning
   Conquered death and burst His grave;
     Showed Himself the mighty Champion,
     Still alive and strong to save.

4. Christ the King, to earth returning,
   Surely will not long delay;
   Christ the Son of God requires us
   Now to trust Him and obey;
     Stands Himself as Lord and Saviour,
     Asking our response today.

© C. Idle and N.L. Warren, 1969. By kind permission.

192 Hush little Baby

Words: P. Malloch
Music: Traditional
arr. D.G. Wilson

Hush little ba-by don't you cry,___ Re-

D Am7

-member Je-sus___ You were born to die___

D G

2. To Your world You came, a Jew;
   But even they rejected You.
   All Your trials, Lord, soon be over.

3. On Your Cross You gave this cry,
   'My God, I am forsaken, why?'
   All Your trials, Lord, soon be over.

4. You died, my Master, You died,
   But You rose again.

5. How can I so careless be,
   Of love which suffered so for me?
   All Your trials, Lord, soon be over.

6. Teach me, Lord, to love men too;
   If they laugh at me, they did worse to You.
   All our trials, Lord, soon be over.

7. Work hard, my brothers, work fast,
   For He's coming soon.
   Then our trials, Lord, shall be over!

193 He is the Way

2. More of the Way - dear Lord, be this my choosing;
    More of the Truth - Lord, teach me day by day;
    More of the Life - for ever satisfying;
    More of Thyself - the Life, the Truth, the Way!

194 I know a name

Words and Music: K.W. Wood

1. I know a name That's nev-er gon-na pass a-way,
2. God said this name Would al-ways be re-membered here,
4. Then you will know The name that's never gon-na die,

Though men may try 'n try 'n try to for-get it,
Here in this world that turned Him a-way,
Then you'll be one of those who pray day by day,

God will nev-er let it die. Je-sus-that's the name
Men would always pray to Him. Je-sus-that's the name
One of those who say like me- Je-sus-that's the name

Son of God who came to die for me.
He who took the blame for all my sins,
Let me spread His fame un-til He comes,

To Coda

Last time

Je - sus- that's the name.
Je - sus- that's the name.
Je - sus- that's the name.

3. And do you

know Him,   this   Je - sus,   as   your own liv-ing Lord?

Am   D7   G   C   G

—   If you want to   know this Je-sus   be - lieve His faith-ful

Am   D7   G   C   G

word.   If   you   call Him   then   be   cer - tain   that your

G   A   G6   Fmaj.7

voice will be heard, He'll come to you, make you free.

195 There was a man

Words and Music: G. McClelland
arr. P. Bye

There was a man from Ga - li - lee He came to die for you and me. He gave His life on Cal - va - ry And now He lives for you and me. I know He lives in me.

2. God sent His Son, His only one,
    To show us love from up above
    To show the way and how to pray
    And how He cares for us each day.
    I know He cares for me.

3. In such a world so full of sin
    Where can we find real peace within
    Where can we find our rock secure
    Where can we find a love so pure?
    Christ is the only one.

196 Jesus from glory

Words: J.E. Seddon
Music: M.A. Baughen and D.G. Wilson

Je - sus from glo - ry to Beth - le - hem came,
Born in a small wayside inn; He who cre - a - ted the
worlds by His pow'r In grace came to save us from sin.

2. Jesus the Word to His own people came,
   Their true Redeemer and King,
   Him they rejected, His truth they despised,
   They spurned all the gifts He would bring.

3. Jesus the Saviour to Calvary came,
   Victim of hatred and strife;
   Flogged and disowned He was nailed to a cross,
   And yet by that death we have life.

4. Jesus the Lord out of death's bondage came,
   Victor o'er Satan and sin,
   Now in His pow'r He will dwell in our lives,
   And help us our victory to win.

5. Jesus the Master to your life will come,
   Bringing salvation and peace;
   In His glad service you'll find your reward
   And pleasures that never shall cease.

6. Jesus the Sovereign in glory shall come,
   Man's full redemption to bring;
   Saints of all ages their Lord shall acclaim,
   Their Saviour, their God and their King.

197 There is no-one in the world like Jesus

Words: M.A. Baughen
Music: N.L. Warren

grac - ious | Friend. There is | no - one in the

Eb6 D7

world like | Je - sus,_____ There is | none that can com-

G Am D7 G

- pare with my____ Lord._____

C G

2. If I go up to the heavens He is there
   If I go down to the depths He's there too
   Anywhere, everywhere,
   Anytime, all the time,
   He is with me evermore.
   Chorus

3. Nothing is this world can ever separate
   The believer from the love of the Lord.
   Death or life, evil powers,
   Present things, coming things,
   None can part us from His love.
   Chorus

F

198 King of kings

Words: D. Brand
Music: M.A. Baughen and N.L. Warren

King of kings and Prince of princes Greatest joy that came to earth Wondrous

Am7 D7   G   Am7 D7   G

love our lives en-circling, Christ div-ine of ho-ly birth. On His

Am7   D7   G   Am   G   D7   G

knee___ He took the chil-dren At His feet the ox-en bowed, From His

Am7   D7   G   Em   Am   D7   G   D7 G7

face there shone a rad-iance Brighter than the whit-est cloud.

C   Am   Bm   Em   Am7   D7   G

2. With His precious blood He saved us,
   On His head He wore a thorn,
   By His hands He hung and suffered,
   Round Him was a cloak all torn.
   With the Father now in heaven,
   Jesus is enthroned on high,
   'Hallelujah', sing the angels,
   'See the King of kings is nigh!'

© D. Brand and M.A. Baughen 1969. By kind permission.

Incarnation and Birth
199 Lord of love

Words: T. Dudley-Smith
Music: N.L. Warren

With-in a crib my Sa - viour lay A wood-en man-ger filled with hay, Come down for love___ on Christ-mas day, All glo - ry be___ to Je - - -sus.

2. Upon a cross my Saviour died,
    To ransom sinners crucified.
    His loving arms still open wide.
    All glory be to Jesus!

3. A victor's crown my Saviour won,
    His work of love and mercy done,
    The Father's high-ascended Son,
    All glory be to Jesus!

200 Holy Child

Words T. Dudley-Smith
Music: M.A. Baughen
arr. D.G. Wilson

1. & 7. Ho - ly child, _____ how still you lie; Safe the man - ger, soft the hay, Faint up- on _____ the East-ern sky Breaks the dawn of Christ - mas day. 2. Ho-ly

Child,_____ whose birth day brings

Shep-herds

Am   D7

from   their field   and   fold,   An - gel

G   Em

choirs   and East - ern   kings,   Myrrh and

Am   Am7

frank - in -cense and   gold._____

D7   C   D7   D7

3. Holy Child, what gift of grace,
   From the Father freely willed
   In your infant form we trace
   All God's promises fulfilled.

4. Holy Child, whose human years
   Span like ours delight and pain,
   One in human joys and tears,
   One in all but sin and stain.

5. Holy Child, so far from home,
   Sons of men to seek and save,
   To what dreadful death you come,
   To what dark and silent grave.

6. Holy Child, before whose Name
   Powers of darkness faint and fall;
   Conquered, death and sin and shame,
   Jesus Christ is Lord of all.

7. Holy Child, how still you lie—
   Safe the manger, soft the hay,
   Clear upon the Eastern sky
   Breaks the dawn of Christmas Day.

© T. Dudley–Smith and M.A. Baughen 1969. By kind permission.

201 Calypso carol

Words: M.A. Perry
Music: S.K. Coates

See Him a - ly-ing on a bed of straw; A draughty sta - ble with an o - pen door, Ma - ry cra - dl - ing the babe she bore; The Prince of Glo - ry is His name.

2. Star of silver sweep across the skies,
   Show where Jesus in the manger lies.
   Shepherds swiftly from your stupor rise
   To see the Saviour of the world.
       Chorus

3. Angels, sing again the song you sang,
   Bring God's glory to the heart of man:
   Sing that Bethlehem's little baby can
   Be Salvation to the soul.
       Chorus

4. Mine are riches - from thy poverty:
   From thine innocence, eternity;
   Mine, forgiveness by thy death for me,
   Child of sorrow for my joy.
       Chorus

202 The road

Words: P. Monk
Music: M.A. Baughen

A ba - by was born in Beth - le - hem by a

sta - ble light: a stran - ger in oc - cu - pied

coun - try on a win - ter night- But the

road runs from Beth - le - hem straight and sto - ny

steep and long: the road runs from

Beth - le - hem through thir - ty years to Cal - va - ry.

Am7   D7   G   C   C6   G   D7   G

2. The baby born in Bethlehem
    Was Jesus Christ, God's Son,
    And when as man our Saviour came
    Redemption was begun –
      But the road runs. . .

3. For He was born in Bethlehem
    Under a winter sky
    To walk the road to Calvary
    There for our sins to die –
      And the road runs. . .

203 O come, O come, Immanuel

Words from: The Great O Antiphons (12th - 13th cent.)
tr. J.M. Neale
Music: D.G. Wilson

O come, O come, Im - man - u - el, And ran - som

Em   Em7   Am   D7   G

cap - tive Is - ra - el, That mourns in lone - ly

Am6   Em   B7   Em   E7

ex - ile here, Un - til the Son of God ap - pear.

A   Em   Em7   C   B

2. O come, O come, Thou Lord of might
    Who to Thy tribes, on Sinai's height
    In ancient times didst give the law
    In cloud and majesty and awe:
        Refrain

3. O come, Thou rod of Jesse, free
    Thine own from Satan's tyranny;
    From depths of hell Thy people save,
    And give them victory o'er the grave:
        Refrain

4. O come, Thou Dayspring, come and cheer
    Our spirits by Thine advent here;
    Disperse the gloomy clouds of night,
    And death's dark shadows put to flight.
        Refrain

5. O come, Thou Key of David, come
    And open wide our heavenly home;
    Make safe the way that leads on high,
    And close the path to misery:
        Refrain

204 In between

Words: R.A. Leaver
Music: D.C. Jeffrey

In be-tween The ho-tel and the road,

In a bor-rowed sta - ble The King comes as fore-told._____ The

man_ in the mid-dle is the one who came for us, As a

ba - by   in   a   cra - dle- And we   nailed Him to   a   cross.

F   Dm9   F   Bb   Am   G

2. In between
   A donkey and a cow,
   In a borrowed manger,
   The King descends so low.
     The man in the middle...

3. In between
   The husband and the wife,
   In a borrowed fam'ly
   The King takes on our life.
     The man in the middle...

4. In between
   The shepherds and the kings;
   Without the borrowed riches
   The King new value brings.
     The man in the middle...

5. In between
   Two crosses on a hill,
   On a borrowed gallows
   For us He pays the bill.
     The man in the middle...

© R.A. Leaver and D.C. Jeffrey, 1969. By kind permission.

205 The Lord of all glory

Words T. Dudley-Smith
Music: M.A. Baughen
arr. D.G. Wilson

Hush   you,   my   ba - by, —   The   night   wind   is

F   C7   F   Dm   Gm7

cold.   The   lambs   from the   hill - side   Are

C7   F   C7   F   Dm

safe   in   the   fold.   Sleep with   the
                                                    cresc.

Gm7   C7   F

star - light   And wake with   the   morn,

Dm   Am   Em   Am

The Lord of   all glo - ry   A ba-by   is   born.

D7   Gm   C7   F

2. Hush you, my baby,
    So soon to be grown,
    Watching by moonlight
    On mountain alone,
    Toiling and travelling -
    So sleep while you can,
    Till the Lord of all glory
    Is seen as a man.

3. Hush you, my baby,
    The years will not stay;
    The cross on the hilltop
    The end of the way.
    Dim through the darkness,
    In grief and in gloom,
    The Lord of all glory
    Lies cold in the tomb.

4. Hush you, my baby,
    The Father on high
    In power and dominion
    The darkness puts by.
    Bright from the shadows,
    The seal and the stone.
    The Lord of all glory
    Returns to His own.

5. Hush you, my baby,
    The sky turns to gold;
    The lambs from the hillside
    Are loose from the fold.
    Fast fades the midnight
    And new springs the morn,
    For the Lord of all glory
    A Saviour is born.

206 The early dawn carol

Words and Melody: S. Beckley
arr. M.C.T. Strover

grip of night____ had well-nigh gone, In a sta - ble

A7

D

bare____ in Ma - ry's care and Jo - seph's, There my Lord was

Em A9 A7

born.____ On a night like this,____ with its star - ry

D9 A7 D

sky, Some shepherds had no time to won - der

E13 A9

why A bril-liant light out of the night, dazzled their sight, and an - gels

D   Em   A9

cry: 'Don't be a - fraid,   but ra-ther joy;   To you this

D6   D   A7

tide   is born a   boy.'—   And now the   message   is un-

D

- furled,   'He came as Sa - viour   to   the world.'

G   Em   D   A7   D   A7

And yet this ba - by had to die,_____ To save a guil - ty sin - ner such as I; And this be - cause_____ up - on the cross He'd take my sins at Cal - va - ry._____

G

207 Christmas for God's holy people

Words: M. Saward
Music: M.A. Baughen
arr. D.G. Wilson

Christ-mas for God's ho-ly peo-ple Is a time of joy and peace, So, good Chris-tian men and wo-men Hymns and car-ols let us raise To our God Come to earth Son of man, by hu-man birth.

2. Child of Mary, virgin mother,
   Peasant baby, yet our king,
   Cradled once midst ass and oxen
   Joyful carols now we sing
   To our God. . . .

3. Angel armies sang in chorus
   To our Christ's nativity
   He who came to share our nature
   So we sing with gaiety
   To our God. . . .

4. Working men ran to the manger,
   Saw the babe of Bethlehem,
   Glorified the God of heaven,
   Now we join to sing with them
   To our God. . . .

5. Infant lowly, born in squalor,
   Prophet, King and great High Priest
   Word of God to man descending
   Still we sing, both great and least
   To our God. . . .

Cross and Resurrection
208 When I survey

Words: Isaac Watts
Music: O Waley, Waley, collected by Cecil J. Sharp.
arr. D.G. Wilson

When I sur-vey the won-drous cross On which the

Prince of Glory died, My rich-est gain I count but

loss, And pour con-tempt on all my pride.

2. Forbid it, Lord, that I should boast
Save in the cross of Christ my God;
All the vain things that charm me most,
I sacrifice them to His blood.

3. See, from His head, His hands, His feet,
Sorrow and love flow mingled down;
Did e'er such love and sorrow meet,
Or thorns compose so rich a crown?

4. Were the whole realm of nature mine,
That were an offering far too small;
Love so amazing, so divine,
Demands my soul, my life, my all.

209 A man died

Words: D.E. Wood
Music: R.K. Price

VERSE
Long years a - go in a far East-ern land, a man died,___ Nails in His hands and His feet and a sword in His side,___ Crowds watched Him die, as He hung on a cross in the gloom. When they took Him down His bo - dy was sealed in a tomb.___

2. The man had said 'after three days I rise from the dead' -
    His enemies the Jews now remembered what He had said.
    They wanted a guard for the tomb for they still feared the man,
    'Go your way', said Pilate, 'and make it as safe as you can.'
    Chorus

3. So soldiers set watch on the tomb all day and all night,
    And on the third day, the women came ere it was light,
    They found the tomb open, no soldiers, the body was gone,
    And inside were two angels who said 'He is risen - God's Son'.
    Chorus

4. The Jews did not find Him, and death could not hold Him, nor the grave,
    For this man is Jesus, Messiah, Almighty to save.
    He was mocked by the crowd, as He died on the cross for their sin,
    But He rose from the dead, a sure hope for all now to win.
    Chorus

5. What is He to you, this Jesus who died in such shame?
    Your Saviour? a good man? or merely a story-book name?
    Own Him as your Saviour, your lips with His praises will ring,
    For one day you must meet Him, as either your Judge or your King.
    Chorus

210 On a hill called Skull

Words: R.P.R. Warren
Music: G. Wilson
arr: G.R. Timms

2. On the tree on the Hill called Skull.
Christ Jesus won the fight,
The Battle then was with Hell,
So day turned black as night.
Not that we knew or asked Him to
In fact we put Him there
Yes, the man
On the tree of the Hill called Skull,
Who stripped the Devil bare.

3. On the tree on the Hill called Skull,
Christ Jesus ripped apart,
That veil which cuts us off from God,
Our selfish wilful heart.
Not that we touch or even reached,
For the friendship of our God
In the man
On the tree on the Hill called Skull,
Whose nail-pierced hand says 'Come'.

4. On the tree on the Hill called Skull,
Christ Jesus once for all,
Put the world to rights that hour,
It's finished was His last call.

211 A hill beside Jerusalem

Words: C.E. Reddin and R.K. Price
Music: R.K. Price

A hill be - side Je - ru - sa - lem, Three

Dm   Am7   Bb   Dm

cross - es stark and free, Mark the place where three men

Dm   C   F   Bb   Gm

slow - ly died-And One there died for you and me.

Am7   Bb6   Dm   Am7   Bb   Dm

2. They hailed Him at Jerusalem's gate,
   And gathered there to see
   The Son of God come riding in -
   But there He died for you and me.

3. A friend betrayed Him to the Jews,
   But death He would not flee;
   They scorned and mocked and spat on Him,
   And there He died for you and me.

4. They led Him up to Calvary's hill,
   And nailed Him to a tree,
   They pierced His side with cruel spear -
   And there He died for you and me.

5. But death our Saviour could not hold,
   For God's own Son was He,
   He rose victorious over sin,
   Because He died for you and me.

212 Do you remember?

Words and Music: The Crossbeats
arr. J. and B. Courtie

Je - sus came down to earth from heav'n a - bove;

C   Am   F   G7

Yes, He came down to earth. Won-der-ful love!

C   Am7   F   G7

Do you re -mem-ber___ long a- go?

C   Am   F   G7

Do you re- mem-ber,___ He loved us so.

C   Am   F   G7

Verse:

1. He did-n't have to come for you and me,
2. He did-n't have to die on Cal - va - ry;

C   Am   F   G7

He wan-ted us to live e - ter-nal - ly
He wan-ted us to live e - ter-nal - ly

C   Am7   F   G7

Do you re -mem-ber tho' you weren't there?
Do you re -mem-ber long,_ a - go?

C   Am   F   G7

Do you re-mem-ber, or don't you care, don't you
Do you re-mem-ber, He loved us so, loved us

C   Am   F   G

care? _____
so! _____ Is it noth-ing to you that Je-sus

Am   G7   F   D7

died? _____ Is it noth-ing that He was cru-ci-

G   E7

-fied?   Can't you be-lieve?

A   G   E

Can't you be-lieve?

F   D   G   G   G7

Do you re-mem-ber,— tho' you weren't there?

C Am F G

Do you re-mem-ber — or don't you care?— Don't you

C Am F G7

care,— don't you care,— don't you care— don't you care? Do you re-

C Am F G7

-member?—

C Am F Db7 C

213 A purple robe

Words: T. Dudley-Smith
Music: D.G. Wilson

1. A pur - ple robe, a crown of thorn, A
4. He hangs, by whom the world was made, Be-

reed in His right hand; Be -
-neath the dark - ened sky; The

-fore the sol - diers' spite and scorn I
ev - er - last - ing ran - som paid, I

see my Sav - iour stand.
see my Sav - iour die.

2. He bears be - tween - the Ro - man guard The
5. He shares on high His Fa - ther's throne, Who

Am Dm Am

weight of all____ our woe;____ A
once in mer - cy came;____ For

C Dm6 Em7 A(sus.4) A

stumb - ling fig - ure bowed and scarred I
all His love to sin - ners shown I

Dm Dm7 B♭6 C

Fine

see my Sav - - iour go. ____
sing my Sav - - iour's Name.____

Dm Am Dm

3. Fast to the cross - - 's spread-ing span,
Dm   C7   F

High in the sun - lit air,
Dm   Am   Dm

All the un - num - bered sins___ of man I
Bb   F   Gm   Dm

D. C. al Fine

see___ my Sav - iour bear.___
Gm7   E7   A(sus.4)   A

214 O Sacrifice of Calvary

Words: M. Saward
Music: W.J. Walter

2. No longer, Saviour, do you plead
Your glorious sacrifice unique,
Yet Lord, in heaven intercede
While I your mercy seek.
Before your Holy Table laid
I kneel once more in love and peace,
Your Blood and Flesh my soul refresh
With joy that shall not cease.

215 'This do', the Master said

Words: M. Saward
Music: M.A. Baughen
arr. D.G. Wilson

This do_____ the Mas- ter said,

This Sac - ra -ment re -peat,

My Bo - - dy and My Blood

In ho - ly sym-bol eat._____ To this great

feast_____ I will in - vite,_____

Am7   D7   G   B7   Em

and   here   u-nite, Both great and   least.   To this great

Am   D9   G

feast_____ I will in - vite _____

Am7   D7   G   B7   Em

and   here   u-nite   both great and   least.'

Am   D7   G

H

2. Don't come, if you would boast
    Your knowledge and your might,
    Don't come, if you refuse
    To serve the Lord of Light.
    But those whose sin
    Has been confessed
    May take their rest
    And join herein.

3. For you, whose sin He bore
    A promise He provides,
    His covenant He makes
    And at His board presides.
    His Sacrifice
    He'll not repeat,
    But take and eat,
    And count the price.

4. One loaf, one body, we,
    One family divine,
    In sweet communion feed
    Upon that Bread and Wine.
    The Great High Priest,
    Until He come
    Has now become
    Our heavenly feast.

5. Then lift your Church to heaven
    Where hunger is no more,
    And through eternity,
    O Christ, we shall adore.
    So make us share
    In glad embrace
    Your matchless grace,
    Both here and there.

216 The third morning

Words: D. Brand
Music: A. Durden

Bright dawned the morn-ing on Geth - se - me-ne's cave,

Cm   Fm7   G

Ma - ry Mag - da - lene came to weep at the grave.

Cm   Fm7   G   Cm

What did she find when she came, full of care? The
stone rolled a-way, and her Mas-ter not there!

Refrain:
Ma-ry, Ma-ry weep-ing at the tomb, Je-sus came and
took a-way her gloom. Je-sus came and took a-way her gloom.

2. 'Where have they taken Him?' poor Mary did pray,
    Crying, and bowing her head in dismay;
    Suddenly in front of her a shadow did fall,
    Mary raised her eyes - 'tis the gardener, that's all. '
    Chorus

3. 'Why are you weeping? Come, tell me your fears. '
    'My Jesus is gone ', she said through her tears.
    'Mary! ' was all that the Person replied,
    Then Mary knew at once that her Lord had not died.
    Chorus

4. Overcome with joy, she touched the hem of His gown,
    Clinging to Jesus, at His feet she fell down.
    'Lord, you're alive! ' was all that Mary could say,
    'This is indeed your Resurrection Day! '
    Chorus

217 It happened in Jerusalem

Words: P. Monk
Music: M.A. Baughen
arr: D.G. Wilson

day.   could-n't it make a lot of sense to-day?

G   C   D7   G   C   D7   G

2. The charge they brought was blasphemy,
   The prisoner was framed,
   And Pilate washed his hands of him –
   But why should he be blamed:
      Chorus

3. They flogged him then and mocked him,
   And dragged him to the Hill
   Through jostling crowds that jeered –
   But why be troubled still:
      Chorus

4. And on that city rubbish-tip
   They nailed him to a cross
   And left him in the sun to die –
   But what's all that to us?
      Chorus

5. Friends left him through the sabbath day
   In a borrowed grave,
   On Sunday morning he had gone –
   But still what does that prove:
   Chorus

6. Alive they say he joined these friends
   And all the nail-marks saw;
   He parted from them heavenwards –
   But how can we be sure:
      Chorus

7. It happened in Jerusalem
   In the early spring;
   They say, God lived and died a man –
   Or some such crazy thing;
      Chorus

218 We shall rise

The group can be divided for this song, so that one half
is singing the chorus while the other half is singing a
verse, and then vice versa.

Words: Anon
Music: Traditional
arr: J.D. Thornton

We shall then be with Him ev - er - more.

C   G7

We shall then be with the Lord, We shall then be with the Lord.

C   C7   F   F#

We shall then be with Him ev - er - more.

C   G7   C

2. Death has lost its sting for us
   Death has lost its sting for us
   Death has lost its sting for evermore
      (repeat)
     Chorus

3. Hallelujahs then will ring
   Hallelujahs then will ring
   Hallelujahs to the Lamb who died
      (repeat)
     Chorus

The Holy Spirit

219 Spirit of God within me

Words T. Dudley-Smith
Music: M.A. Baughen
arr. D.G. Wilson

Spir - it   of God with - in   me,

pos-sess   my hu - man   frame;   Fan the dull

em - bers   of   my heart   Stir up   the liv - ing

flame.   Strive till   that im - age

Ad - am lost, New min - ted and re - stored

F# B7 E C#m F#m B7

In shin - ing splen - dour bright - ly bears The like - ness

E E maj.7 A F#m G#m C#m7

vv 1-3 | v4

of___ the Lord. day.

F#m B7 E E

2. Spirit of truth within me,
Possess my thought and mind;
Lighten anew the inward eye
By Satan rendered blind;
Shine on the words that wisdom speaks
And grant me power to see
The truth made known to men in Christ,
And in that truth be free.

3. Spirit of love within me,
Possess my hands and heart;
Break through the bonds of self-concern
That seeks to stand apart:
Grant me the love that suffers long,
That hopes, believes and bears,
The love fulfilled in sacrifice,
That cares as Jesus cares.

4. Spirit of life within me,
Possess this life of mine;
Come as the wind of heaven's breath,
Come as the fire divine!
Spirit of Christ, the living Lord,
Reign in my house of clay,
Till from its dust with Christ I rise
To everlasting day.

220 Fire of God

Words: M. Saward
Music: D.G. Wilson

Fire of God, ti - tan - ic Spir - it,

Burn with - in our hearts to - day,

Cleanse our sin; may we ex - hib - it

Ho - li - ness in ev - 'ry way.

Purge the squal - id - ness that shames us,

Soils the bo - dy; taints the soul.

A7 / D

And through Je - sus Christ who claims us,

Dm   Dm7   G7   G9   Em   G7   C maj.9   C

Last time

Pu - ri - fy us; make us whole.

F   F maj.7   C   Dm7 G7   C

2. Wind of God, dynamic Spirit,
   Breathe upon our hearts today
   That we may Your power inherit
   Hear us, Spirit, as we pray.
   Fill the vacuum that enslaves us,
   Emptiness of heart and soul,
   And, through Jesus Christ who saves us,
   Give us life and make us whole.

3. Voice of God, prophetic Spirit,
   Speak to every heart today,
   To encourage or prohibit,
   Urging action or delay.
   Clear the vagueness which impedes us,
   Come, enlighten mind and soul.
   And, through Jesus Christ who leads us,
   Teach the truth that makes us whole.

© M. Saward 1968 and D.G. Wilson 1969. By kind permission.

221 He's the Comforter

Words and Music: R.T. Bewes
arr. M.C.T. Strover

He was there when earth was hurled in space, By man or beast un-trod. He was mov-ing ov-er the wa-ter's face, The un-seen Spir-it of God.

CHORUS

He's the Com-for-ter, He's the breath of God, He's the wind of rushing mighty pow'r. He gives strength to win When He dwells with-in Mak-ing Je-sus real ev-'ry hour.

C6   Am7   C   D7   G6

2. He was there of old and gave God's Word.
Inspired both sage and youth;
The apostles wrote what they'd seen and heard,
Led by the Spirit of Truth.
Chorus

3. He was there in fire on the Church outpoured,
His gifts and power sufficed;
He reminded men of their reigning Lord,
The living Spirit of Christ.
Chorus

4. He is here to give new birth, and still
The clamour and the strife;
Let us grieve Him not but seek His will,
Dynamic Spirit of Life!
Chorus

222 If you've asked

Words and Music: D.B. Pettinger

1. If you've asked my Je-sus___ To be your Sav-iour___

C   G7   C7   F   Bb   C7   F

___ You will know the Spir-it's pow'r with-in.___

Dm   Am   Gm   C7   G7   C7   F

He will want to change you___ To make you like your Lord___

C   G7   C7   F   Bb   F   A7   Dm

Giv - ing you vic - t'ry ov - er sin.

Dm   C6   Bb6   C   G   C7   F

Chorus:
Yes, guid-ance comes from God the Ho - ly Spir - it

C7   G7   C7   F   Bb   F

Let Him con - trol your life from day to day;

C   G7   C

Just seek His will in pray'r You'll find He's al - ways there

C7   G7   C7   F   Bb   C7   F   A7   Dm

To help you find God's per - fect way.

C6   Bb6   C   G7   C7   F

2. Do you know the answer
   To all the problems
   You may have to face this very day?
   Jesus sent His Spirit
   To live within your heart
   To hear and guide you when you pray.
   Chorus

3. Is your life as useful
   As God desires it?
   Is He satisfied with all you do?
   Seek the Spirit's guidance
   And He will show you all
   The Lord your God has planned for you.
   Chorus

The Second Coming

223 When the Lord

2. When the Lord is seen again
   Not the glories of His reign,
   Not the lightnings through the storm,
   Not the radiance of His form,
   Not His pomp and power alone,
   Not the splendours of His throne,
   Not His robe and diadems,
   Not the gold and not the gems,
   But His face upon my sight
   Shall be darkness into light -
     But His face upon my sight
     Shall be darkness into light.

3. When the Lord to human eyes
   Shall bestride our narrow skies,
   Not the child of humble birth,
   Not the carpenter of earth,
   Not the man by men denied,
   Not the victim crucified,
   But the God who died to save,
   But the victor of the grave,
   He it is to whom I fall,
   Jesus Christ, my All in all -
     He it is to whom I fall,
     Jesus Christ, my All in all.

I

224 He's coming

Words and Music: The Crossbeats
arr: J. and B. Courtie

He's com-ing;   My Je-sus is   com-ing,

C   E7   Am   G7   G

My Je-sus is   com-ing,   He's com-ing for you and

F   C   Dm   Fm   G7

me.   When He went a-way   He told us to

Am   G7   C   E7   Am   G7

watch and pray,   For He said He'd come back some day.   He's

C   F   C

com-ing for you and me. He's coming a-gain.

Dm Fm G7 C C7 F

Can't you see that He died for you and He died for me? He

C

wants us to live e- ter- nal - ly. So if heav-en's not your

F C Dm

home,— You can take Him as your own. He's com-ing;

G Dm G7 C

me.   But when He comes a-gain__ Will He

Am   G7   C

take you then, Or will He leave you here   with oth-er men? Now are you

E7   Am   G7   C   F

⊕ CODA

rea-dy?   Are you rea-dy to go with Him?   coming for you and

C   Dm Fm G7   C   Dm Fm G7

me.   He's coming for you   and   me.

Am   Dm Fm G7   C   C6

© Sky Sounds. By kind permission.

225 Is He satisfied?

day should be the end and e - ter - ni - ty be -
boasts of wealth and pow'r none can help him in that

F   F7   Bb

-gin, When the book is op -ened wide, Would the
hour When the an - gels hear his plea; Is He

F   C7   F   Bb

CHORUS

Lord be sat - is - fied. Is He
sat - is - fied with me?

F   C7   F   F

sat - is - fied, is He sat - is - fied?

F7   Bb   F°

THE SECOND COMING

men, what if ev - 'ry friend He had were just like me? _____

Dm   A7   Dm   G7   C7   G7♭5

_____ Would He feel a wel - come here or would He

C7   F   F7

go a - way in tears? Am I all that I should

B♭   B°   F

be?_ Is He sat - is - fied with me? 2. Fee-ble me?

B♭ B♭m F C7   F   C7   F

226 When He comes

Words: T. Dudley-Smith
Music: J.D. Thornton

1. When He comes When He comes We shall see the Lord in glo-ry when He comes, As I read the gos-pel sto-ry We shall see the Lord in glo-ry, We shall see the Lord in glo-ry when He comes! With the

2. When He comes,
    When He comes,
    We shall hear the trumpet sounded when He comes,
    We shall hear the trumpet sounded,
    See the Lord by saints surrounded,
    We shall hear the trumpet sounded when He comes!
        With the Alleluias ringing to the sky,
        With the Alleluias ringing to the sky,
        We shall hear the trumpet sounded,
        See the Lord by saints surrounded,
        With the Alleluias ringing to the sky!

3. When He comes,
    When He comes,
    We shall all rise up to meet Him when He comes,
    When He calls His own to greet Him
    We shall all rise up to meet Him,
    We shall all rise up to meet Him when He comes.
        With the Alleluias ringing to the sky,
        With the Alleluias ringing to the sky,
        When He calls His own to greet Him,
        We shall all rise up to meet Him,
        With the Alleluias ringing to the sky.

4. Repeat verse 1

© T. Dudley-Smith and J.D. Thornton 1969. By kind permission.

227 Jesus shall return

Words: P. Monk
Music: M.A. Baughen
arr: M.C.T. Strover

Gently

Once He came un-re-cog-nized, A man by men He

was des-pised, Once for our sin

an-gels   And the songs   of suns and plan-ets   And

Bb   G7   C7

ev - 'ry voice in Cre - a - tion shall be His wel-come then.

F   Fmaj.7   F7   D7   G   C7   F

2. Once He had a human birth
    And lived like us upon this earth
    Knew human grief and human mirth:
        But..but..He shall return in glory
        But..but..He shall return as King-
    And sorrow banished for ever,
    And joy multiplied for ever,
    And human laughter in heaven,
    Shall be His fanfare then.

3. Once He suffered human pain,
    Felt sun and wind, the storm and rain,
    Tempted like us again and again
        But..but..He shall return in glory
        But..but..He shall return as King-
    And the earth become His footstool,
    And the sun a gem in His crown,
    And Satan thrown down defeated,
    Shall be His trophies then.

4. Once He passed through agony
    Knew conflict in Gethsemane
    Then hung exposed, nailed to a tree:
        But..but..He shall return in glory
        But..but..He shall return as King-
    And all knees shall bow in His name
    Every tongue confess Him as Lord,
    And all His children around Him
    Shall be His victory then.

Missionary and Social Concern

228 People I meet

Words and Music: **M. Whitten**

When I look a-round me This is the truth I see Peo-ple are

suff-'ring the whole world through. I look the oth-er way,

Think of my-self a-lone, Knowing what I ought to do.___

2. When I have this world's goods -
   Standards of living high
   One of the 'haves' rather than the 'have-nots',
   Grant me the grace to give,
   Open my heart in love,
   Tackling the world's trouble spots.

3. Help me to feed the hungry
   And give the thirsty drink.
   Caring for strangers and those alone.
   Help me to visit all
   Those who may need a call
   Helping some to make a home.

4. When the son of man comes,
   All nations gathered there,
   To those He welcomes He then will say,
   'I assure you that your deed
   To my brothers in their need
   Was a deed you did to Me'.

229 Send the collecting man from your gate

Words and Music: G. H. Reid
arr: D.G. Wilson

Send the col - lect - ing man | from your gate 'But

C7 F6 F

is - n't the world in a | dread-ful state?'

G G7 C

2. Sitting right there in your sprung settee
   Watching the TV show
   Seeing the struggle to set men free
   Watching it blow-by-blow.
   But the cost of living is getting you down
   You can't even spare a half-a-crown.
   Send the collecting man from your gate
   'But isn't the world in a dreadful staté'.

3. Sitting right there in your favourite chair
   After a three-course meal
   Seeing the suffering everywhere
   Watching the wealthy steal.
   But your rates go up and they freeze your pay
   You can't get abroad for your holiday
   Send the collecting man from your gate
   'But isn't the world in a dreadful state?'

K

230 Black or white, sir

Words and Music : G. C. H. Roberts *arr.* M. Atkin

Black or white, sir?__ This ques-tion re-lates to much more than

Em   Am   Am7   Dm   E7

cof - fee   Or bread on our plates.   It po - ses a choice   be-

Am   Am7   Dm   E7   Am   E7

-tween two ex-tremes Af - fec-ting the mem-bers of our tour-ing teams; De-

Am   E7   Am

-ci-ding who gets the pick of the jobs and who runs the world,   the

Am7   Dm   E7   Am   Am7

'wogs' or the 'nobs'. It's as fier-y as touchwood, we can-not ig -nore, or think all we need is a change in the law; It's men's hearts that dif-fer, some warm and some cold, What-ev - er the col-our of skin we be-hold.

2. Love or hate, sir?
   I ask you to say;
   Please do not take long now,
   There's no middle way;
   Just think if you'd happened to be born jet black -
   You'd want men to pay you, not give you the sack;
   Remember who carried the cross of our Lord:
   For he was an African forced by a sword;
   There won't be a conflict in Britain's small land,
   If different races can live hand-in-hand;
   When we get to heaven, without any doubt,
   No skin will be there to point us all out!

231 The people in between

Words adapted: from an original poem by
an undergraduate of Clare College, Cambridge.
Music: **M.A. Baughen**

1. In the Mis - sion____ near the front, all is
qui - et: it is night: Then the guns be-hind the house be-gin to
pound and in their light The___ man - y huts of straw, the frightened
fa -ces, can be seen,— The fa-ces of the Peo-ple In Be- tween.

2. They have left their mountain dwellings, where they could no longer stay:
They are sick and they are weary, and their children die each day,
For there's little rice to eat, and no way of keeping clean -
No comfort for the People In Between.

3. These people are not fighting men, they're labourers by birth
They only wished for peace, to share the good things of the Earth.
But their cattle disappeared, and the crops were brown, not green -
No living for the People In Between.

4. What do they know of politics, the clash of East and West?
Both promising the people that 'Our side can serve you best'
But while the war drags on, it seems that neither side is keen
To stop, and help the People In Between.

5. The Hospital is crowded, and the orderlies are few:
They carry on because they know they have a job to do.
A Minister was killed last week, a man of God who'd been
Just trying to help the People In Between.

6. When fighting is the order, then the money's always there
But those who offer comfort find that Government don't care,
It's up to you and me to help, and show them that we mean
Our pity for the People In Between.

© Music by M.A. Baughen 1969 By kind permission.

232 Tell all the world of Jesus

Words: J.E. Seddon
Music: W.J. Walter

His sal - va - tion sing. Tell all men of His

Bb F C7 A7 Dm G7 C7

great - - -ness, In na - ture and in grace; Cre-

F Dm G7 C7 A7 Dm C7

-a - tor and re - dee - mer, The Lord of time and space.

F A7 Dm Am7 D7 Gm Dm C7 F

2. Tell all the world about Jesus,
   That men in Him may find
   The joy of His forgiveness,
   True peace of heart and mind.
   Tell all men of His goodness,
   His deep, unfailing care;
   Of love so rich in mercy,
   A love beyond compare.

3. Tell all the world about Jesus,
   That everyone may know
   Of His almighty triumph
   O'er every evil foe.
   Tell all men of His glory,
   When sin is overthrown,
   And He shall reign in splendour,
   The King upon His throne.

233 Is there an answer

Words and Music: The Kinsmen
arr: The Settlers and M.C.T. Strover

Last time to Coda

VERSE

Lis- ten to the wind of con - science call. 1. There's

E   G#m   F#m   B13   E   C#m7   B7

two thirds of the world go hun-gry ev-'ry night,

E   C#m

Lis - ten to the wind of con - science call____ While

A   B

we un-con-cerned sit and watch the fire - light,

E   C#m

Is there an ans-wer to it all?

2. A man has to fight to gain his civil right,
   Listen to the wind of conscience call,
   While we unconcerned sit and watch the firelight,
   Is there an answer to it all?
   Chorus

3. They crucified a man because they thought He might
   Make us listen to the wind of conscience call.
   While we inconcerned sit and watch the firelight,
   And He is the answer to it all.

   Chorus
   He is the answer to it all, He is the answer to it all,
   We can all be so responsible,
   He is the answer to it all;
   We can all be so responsible,
   Listen to the wind of conscience call.

234 As for our world

Words: T. Dudley-Smith
Music: M.A. Baughen
arr. D.G. Wilson

give us eyes to see   The orph - aned

Gm7   C7   F   Cm7   C7

child,   the   starved and ref - u - gee,

F   Bb   F

The   sick and lame: For sad and

F   G7   C   Bb6

need - - y   chil - dren ev - 'ry - where___

F   Dm   Gm7   C7   F

For this our world, we lift our

hands in pray'r.

C7

2. As for our world we lift our hearts in praise,
The joy of home with lights and hearth ablaze,
    The welcome plain;
So we recall the homeless and the cold,
The destitute, the prisoners, and the old
    Who lie in pain:
For all who grieve, for all who know despair -
For this our world, we lift our hands in prayer.

3. As for our world we lift our hearts in praise,
Recount the blessings that our life displays
    In every part,
So look in mercy, Lord, where shadows rest,
The ravaged homes by want and wars oppressed,
    The sick at heart.
With burdens more than man was meant to bear -
For this our world, we lift our hands in prayer.

4. As for our world we lift our hearts in praise,
The love of God on all our works and ways,
    So we commend
All those who loveless live and hopeless mourn,
Who die at last uncomforted, forlorn,
    Without a friend;
Who own no Saviour's love, no Father's care -
For this our world, we lift our hands in prayer.

5. As for our world we lift our hearts in praise,
So with our songs of thankfulness we raise
    This ageless plea:
That darkened souls who have no song to sing
May find in Christ the living Lord and King
    He came to be;
And in His cross and resurrection share -
For this our world, we lift our hands in prayer.

Prayer and the Word

235 Meet the Saviour

Prayerfully

Words and Music: G. Brattle

Meet Je - sus in the morn - ing, As day is breaking through; Meet Je - sus in the noon - tide, He'll talk a - gain with you; Meet Je - sus in the ev - 'ning, As thoughts are turned to rest; Be sure to meet the Sav-iour, And ev - 'ry day is blest!

236   An all-day faith

Words: D. Brand
Music: A. Durden

Chorus:

It's an all day faith you must have in your Lord, It's an all day faith you must have in your Lord, It's an all day faith you must have in your Lord, For He loves you all the day long. loves you all the day long.

To verse:

To finish

A little slower

In the quiet of the morn - ing give some time to Him,

E C#m F#m7 B7

Pray-ing that He will en - rich you with-in, For - give and de-li-ver you from

A E B7 E G#m

all of your sin Yes the morn-ing you must give to your Lord.

E7 A7 E F#m7 E6 B7 E A E

2. In the heat of the noon-day put your faith in your God,
    Knowing that He's there as your Staff and your Rod,
    As you walk in the Way, tread the steps that He trod;
    Yes, the noon-day you must give to your Lord.
        Chorus

3. In the cool of the evening commune with the Son,
    Telling Him all about all you have done.
    Sharing your sorrows and recounting your fun;
    Yes, the evening you must give to your Lord.
        Chorus

237   Hands of Jesus

Words and Music: G. Brattle

Smoothly

1. Hands of Je - sus, take the bread,

As long a - go While here be - low;

Take the bread___ at morn - ing time.

2.   Hands of Jesus, bless the bread;
   Bless it to me,
   That it may be
   Living bread at morning time.

3.   Hands of Jesus, break the bread,
   And break it small,
   And grant to all
   Broken bread at morning time.

4.   Hands of Jesus, give the bread,
   That with Thy Word,
   We may be fed;
   Hear our prayer at morning time.

*   The word 'evening' may be used when applicable.

238 Open my ears

Based on words by: S.N. Davies
Music: J.A. Cox

1. Op - en my ears to your Word Lord of my life, I pray, That as I seek to serve you I may hear what you say.

2. Open my eyes to your Word
That as I read each day,
New things I may discover
To help me walk your way.

3. Open my heart to your Word
That as I read today
My heart may not be hardened
But will with joy obey.

© S.N. Davies and J.A. Cox 1969. By kind permission.

L

239 Kingdoms may rise

Words and Music: J. Lorimer Gray and D. Kennedy
arr: D.G. Wilson

word of the Lord en - du -reth for ev - er - more.

E7   A   D

To finish   *Fine*   To continue

Take God at His prom-ise

A   A7   D   A

put your faith in Christ   Trust Him for sal -

E7   A   B7

D. S. al Fine

- va - tion And e - - ter - - nal life!

E   E7

240 What a friend

Words: J.M. Scriven
Music: 'The carnival is over' by Tom Springfield

Slow 4 (with a beat)

What a friend____ we have in Je - sus All our sins____ and grief to bear!____ What a priv - - - i-lege to car - ry Ev - 'ry thing____ to God in pray'r.____ O what peace____ we of - ten for - feit, O what need - - less pain we bear_____ All be-

-cause_____ we do not car - ry Ev - 'ry thing_____ to God in

pray'r!_____ 2. Have we trials_____ and temp - ta - tions? Is there

trou - - - - - ble ev - 'ry - where?_____ We should

knows⸺ our ev - 'ry weak - - ness: Take it

Bb   C7   F   Dm

1
to⸺ the Lord in pray'r.   Are we pray'r.⸺

Bb   C7   F   C7   F

3.   Are we weak and heavy-laden,
     Cumbered with a load of care?
     Jesus only is our refuge:
     Take it to the Lord in prayer.
     Do thy friends despise, forsake thee?
     Take it to the Lord in prayer;
     In His arms He'll take and shield thee!
     Thou wilt find a solace there.

4.   What a friend we have in Jesus,
     All our sins and grief to bear!
     What a privilege to carry
     Everything to God in prayer.
     O what peace we often forfeit,
     O what needless pain we bear
     All because we do not carry
     Everything to God in prayer.

© Music, Springfield Music Ltd., 1965. By kind permission.

241 In the stillness

Words and Music: G. Brattle

Light and Rhythmic

In the still - ness of the morn - ing,   May Thy

F7   Bb   Eb   C7

* The word evening may be used when applicable.

voice a - lone be heard;⸻ In the quiet-ness of Thy

F7   Bb   B   F7   Bb

pres- ence May we hear God's liv - ing Word. In the one-ness of the

Eb   C7 F7   Bb   Eb

Spi - rit We would wait up - on Thee, Lord;⸻ In the

Bb   C7   F7

still -ness of the morn-ing, May Thy blessing be out- poured.

Bb   Eb G7 Cm C7 F   F7 Bb

© G. Brattle 1969. By kind permission.

Dedication and Response

242 What He wants me

Words adapted and Music: N.L. Warren

What He wants me, He can make me, Where He wants me,
G   Am7   D9   Bm7   Em9   Am7

He can take me, But He nev-er will for-sake me,
D7   G9   C9   E7   Am   D7

For I am His own. Now my life be-
Eb7   D7   G   Am7

-longs to Je-sus, I am His and He is mine.
Em   G7   C   C6   D7   G

2. Gracious Lord who died to save me,
Bore my sins, in love forgave me,
Life and joy and peace He gave me,
For I am His own.
Now my life belongs to Jesus,
I am His and He is mine.

3. In His mercy Jesus needs me,
With the light of Heaven He leads me,
With the Bread of Life He feeds me,
For I am His own.
Now my life belongs to Jesus.
I am His and He is mine.

243 Now this is just the reason why

Words: from Romans 12. 1. J.H. Coulson
Music: J.G. Coulson

Now this is just the rea-son why I'm tell-ing you To pre-sent your - selves, give your lives to God To be a liv - ing sac - ri -fice that's ho - - ly And ac - cep - ta - ble un - - to Him.

So - this is just the reason why...

2.   He sent His Son and He sent Him just for you,
     Who gave His life, and He gave it all for you
     Just think of all that His love would do yet for you.

And - that is just the reason why...

244 Don't let the world around

Words: from Romans 12. 2. J.H. Coulson
Music: J.G. Coulson (written primarily for the accordion)

Verse:

'Bow down, be like all the rest!' So Daniel's friends were

told. Daunt - less they faced the fi - nal test God

brought them through that fire like gold.

Chorus:

Don't let the world a - round squeeze you in - to that
All through His Word it's told how God makes us

same old mould, | Let | God | re- | mould | your
free and bold | To | stand | life's | pres - | sures,

G   C   G

1

lives | from | with- | in.
with - out | giv - | ing

2

in.

D7   D6   G   G   D.C.

Single, David faced the giant,
Faith backed the stone he threw
Hear, too, Jonathan defiant -
'God saves by many or by few!'
Chorus
'Don't let the world around squeeze you into that same old mould,
Let God remould your lives from within.'
Why fight the fight alone, claim strength from God's own Son,
Whether by few or many He'll win.

Samson, though a mighty giant
And man of God it seems
Though called to serve the Lord his God
Falls before Delilah's schemes.
Chorus
'Don't let the world around squeeze you into that same old mould,
Let God remould your lives from within.'
Don't let them, friend or foe, draw you from the One you know,
Stay close to Jesus through thick or thin.

Joseph, just a slave to sell,
Gideon, poor farmer's boy,
Rebekah, working at the well -
For each fulfillment was God's plan.
Chorus
'Dont let the world around squeeze you into that same old mould,
Let God remould your lives from within.'
Obey His gracious Word, in everything make Him Lord,
Run the straight race with eyes fixed on Him.

245 If I tried

Words and Music: J. McKenzie
arr: N.L. Warren

1. If I tried to live——— for You Lord, to-

-day,——— If I tried to fol - low Your won - der - ful

way, Then all of my life would be me and not

You——— And none of Your glo - ry would

ev - er shine through.

you.

Melody for 2nd Verse begins:

Since I first met You,— I knew, Lord, You were the way,

2. Since I first met You, I knew Lord You were the way,
   I tried hard to walk in Your footsteps each day,
   But somehow my life didn't glorify Thee,
   So make me a channel, and You live through me.

3. Take each new day, whatever's in store,
   Take my whole being and into me pour,
   Your power, and Your Spirit, Oh make me anew,
   For no-one can change me, Lord Jesus, but You.

246 Just as I am

Words: C. Elliott (1789-1871)
Music: P.M. Verrall

But that Thy blood was shed for me,

And that Thou bidd'st me come to Thee, O

Lamb of God, I come.

2. Just as I am, poor, wretched, blind, -
   Sight, riches, healing of the mind,
   Yea, all I need, in Thee to find,
   O Lamb of God, I come,

3. Just as I am, Thou wilt receive,
   Wilt welcome, pardon, cleanse, relieve;
   Because Thy promise I believe,
   O Lamb of God, I come.

4. Just as I am - Thy love unknown
   Has broken every barrier down -
   Now to be Thine, yea, Thine alone,
   O Lamb of God, I come.

5. Just as I am, of that free love
   The breadth, length, depth and height to prove,
   Here for a season, then above, -
   O Lamb of God, I come.

247 Jesus grant that we may follow

Words: J. Young
Music: Traditional
arr: D.G. Wilson

Je - sus, grant that we may fol - low In our
Mas - ter, teach us how to fol - low On the

lives, the steps You trod; With Your life our in - spir -
road to Cal - va - ry. May Your mind be formed a -

1. - a - tion And our pat - tern, Son of God.

2. -mong us, From self- in - t'rest set us free.

2. Lord, we know we cannot follow
Till You save us from our sin.
May the fullness of Your Spirit
Give us risen power within.
Saviour, give us strength to follow
Your example and Your law;
Loving You above all others,
Others may we love the more.

3. Jesus, give us faith to follow
Through affliction, pain and toil.
In the dangerous times of plenty
Keep us faithful, true and loyal.
Peace in turmoil, strength in testing,
Patience in the slower hours;
Joy in life and love in all things,
These were Yours - Lord, make them ours.

Guidance

248   I know the Lord is leading me

Words: H. Kobler
tr: S. Lonsdale and M.A. Baughen
Music: H. Kobler

ev - 'ry prob - lem of my life_____ He
guides me I know the Lord is
lead - - - ing me._____

2. It is the Saviour leading me
   Who rose from death triumphantly
   To whom all power in heaven and earth is given
   It is the Saviour leading me.

3. I trust my God in leading me
   Who said all things will work to be
   For good to those He calls, who love Him truly
   I trust my God in leading me.

249 The Lord is near you

Words and Music: N.L. Warren

The Lord is near___ you___ ___ right by your side. He'll nev-er leave you,___ ___ He is your Guide. Through doubt and sad - - ness,___ ___ In trials and lone - li-ness,

The Lord is near____ you, right by your side. day. The Lord is near____ you,____ right by____ your side.____

Am   G   Cmaj.9

1 & 2   3

G   Em   G   Em   G

G6   Gmaj.7   G6   G   C   G

2. The Lord will live in you, right in your heart.
    His peace He'll give you, His love impart.
    He will cleanse your sin away
    He will teach you how to pray
    When Jesus lives in you, right in your heart.

3. The Lord will come for you, at that Last Day,
    When Heaven will open its shining way.
    Will you be ready then?
    Will you be trusting Him?
    When Jesus comes again, at that Last Day.

    The Lord is near you, right by your side.

250 Wherever He goes

Words and Music: A. Culverwell

help I'll be strong, I will go just where- ev - er He
still trust and pray, I will go just where- ev - er He

G7   D   D   A7

Fine

goes.
goes.   } 2.He may lead me to

D   D7   G

coun - tries where trou - bles sur - round; ev - en

G   D

251 If you know the Lord

Words and Music: B. Reichner

If you know the Lord, ____ You need no-bo-dy else, ____ To see you through ____ the dark-est night. ____

head - in' home____ He'll show you the way.____

If you know the Lord,____ You need no-

-bo - dy else____ to see the light,____ His won- der - ful

light,____ If you know the light.____

252 My Lord's in charge of my life

Words and Music: R. Germain

2. I put my life in His hands, His hands,
   I put my life in His hands
   A slave to Him I am fully free
   I put my life in His hands.

3. He's got a wonderful plan, for me,
   He's got a wonderful plan
   My future's safe though I cannot see
   For He's got a wonderful plan.

4. I'll trust my wonderful Lord, my Lord,
   I'll trust my wonderful Lord
   He cannot fail and He cares for me
   I'll trust my wonderful Lord.

Christian Living

253 The happy people

Words and Music: C. Blissard-Barnes

Hap-py, those,_____ who know they're poor, For the

King - - dom now is theirs, Hap-py, those_____ whose grief is

sore,_____ For God will wipe a-way their tears.

2. Happy, those who are the meek,
   They'll inherit all the earth;
   Happy, those who truly seek
   And hunger for His righteousness and worth.

3. For the Saviour whom they know,
   Always satisfies their heart;
   Happy those who mercy show,
   For they'll obtain God's mercy for their part.

4. Happy, you, the pure in heart,
   You will see God in His Heaven;
   Happy, too, the folk whose lot
   It is to bring true peace to men.

5. This great blessing shall be theirs,
   In the glory soon to come;
   They shall all be called God's heirs,
   When God the Father calls us to His Home.

6. Happy, now, you are when men
   Speak against you for my cause;
   You shall have a place in heaven,
   And great reward shall then be yours.

254 It's not an easy road

Words and Music: S. Beckley
arr: D.G. Wilson

It's not an ea-sy road we are trav-el-ling to hea-ven, For

man- y are the thorns on the way; It's

not an ea - sy road but the Sav -iour is with us, His

pres- ence gives us joy ev - 'ry day.

No no it's not an ea-sy road No

G D9 G C G C G D9

No it's not an ea-sy road; But Je-sus walks beside me and

G C G D7 G G7

brightens the journey, and lightens ev-'ry hea-vy load.

C G D7 G

2. It's not an easy road, there are trials and troubles,
   And many are the dangers we meet;
   But Jesus guards and keeps so that nothing can harm us,
   And smooths the rugged path for our feet.
   Chorus

3. Though I am often footsore and weary from travel,
   Though I am often bowed down with care;
   A better day is coming when home in the glory,
   I'll rest in perfect peace over there.
   Chorus

255 The heavenly way

Words and Music: B.J. Stephenson

While trav-el-ling on the heav'n- - ly way   I know I'll al-ways need God's prec-ious Word, which is my sword, And prayer which is my shield. My Sav-iour's pres-ence keeps and guides Through

-out each pas - sing day I'll nev-er fear the

C6   G   C6

path - - way A - long that heav'n- ly way.

G   Am7 D7 G

2. He's always there beside me
On every mountain side
All thoughts of stumbling flee from me
With Jesus as my guide.
For every footstep that I take
I know He took before
My only wish along the way
Is that I'll know Him more.

3. I read my Bible on the way
To keep me on the road
For if I falter either way
Many snares abound.
I keep in touch with Him by prayer
To keep me free from sin.
I long for that tremendous day
When I can be with Him.

4. For at the end of this same road
There is a place, He said,
Prepared for those who trust in Him
Risen from the dead.
'Worthy the Lamb' my lips will cry
When I before Him come
For ever in His family
When I arrive at home.

256 My sheep hear my voice

Music: J. van den Hogen
arr: D.G. Wilson

My sheep hear my voice and I know them and they fol - low me, and they fol - low me, My sheep hear my voice and I know them and they fol - - low me.

Fine

257 Invisible chains

Words: P. Monk
Music: M.A. Baughen
arr: M.C.T. Strover

These chains are invisible, But these chains are real -

The chains of sin as strong as steel:

As strong as steel You can't see

Chains of sin hold-ing me. In-vis-i-ble

chains, hold-ing me fast,

How long, my Lord, shall this bondage last? In - vis - i - ble

Chains_____ holding me fast,_____ How long, my

Lord, shall this bondage last. Lord, may this freedom last.

2. God's power is visible,
   And God's power is real -
   The power of love stronger than steel;
   Stronger than steel
   - Can't you see? -
   Power of Love
   Sets me free.

   Invisible chains, holding me fast,
   - And now, my Lord, is my bondage past?

3. God's chains are invisible,
   God's chains are real -
   Chains of love stronger than steel:
   Stronger than steel
   - You can see -
   Chains of Love
   Holding me free.

   Invisible chains, holding me fast
   - Forever, Lord, may this freedom last?

258 Each new day, Lord

Words and Music: M.G. Schneider
tr: S. Lonsdale and M.A. Baughen

Each new day, Lord,

F   Fmaj.7

I give it back in-to Your hands for You gave it to me

Dm7   Gm7   C7   F   Fmaj.7 Dm   Bb6 C7 F6

You, my Lord, are the source of time and of its end - ing, I am

F   Fmaj.7   Dm7   Gm7   C7   F   Bb Fmaj.7 Dm

You make darkness light. Each new day, Lord,   I give   it back   in-to Your

Dm   Cm7   F   Cm   F   Fmaj.9 Fmaj.7   Dm7   Gm7   C7

hands for   You gave   it   to   me   You, my   Lord, are

F   Bb   Fmaj.7   Dm   Bb6   C7   Bb   F   Fmaj.7

the source of time and of its end - ing, I am

trust-ing You.

I am trust - ing You.__

Fmaj.⁷   Dm   B♭   C7   B♭   F

2. When a day is finished and I look back
   I have often failed you - with sins that are black
   Yet You cleanse me, O Lord.
   Chorus

3. Many words would have been - better unsaid
   Hardly any thanking - but grumbling instead
   Lord You know what I'm like.
   Chorus

4. Life is all so pointless, lived without You,
   Yet You give it purpose when you're leading me.
   My path you know, O Lord.
   Chorus

259   Please don't ever let me look back

Words and Music: C. Burns
arr. D.G. Wilson

1 & 4. Dark was my night with-out you Lord.
2. Long were those years of my blind - - - ness

F   Am   Cm   D

Long was that nev - er end-ing track.
Strong were those chains a - cross my back.

Gm   F

Thank You for find-ing me.
Thank You for sav-ing me.
Thank You for guiding me. But
Thank You for lov-ing me. But

B♭   F   Dm

To repeat

please don't ev - er let me look back.
please don't ev - er let me look look

G7   C9   C7   F   Gm7   C7

260 We shall overcome

Christ I do be - lieve

C F G6 G7 Am

We shall ov - er - come some day.

C F Dm C G7 C

In verses 2 & 3, lines 1, 2 & 3 begin on the last crotchet of the preceding bar:-

etc.

The truth will make us

2. The truth will make us free,
   The truth will make us free,
   The truth will make us free some day;
   By faith in Christ I do believe
   We shall overcome some day.

3. The Lord will see us through,
   The Lord will see us through,
   The Lord will see us through some day.
   By faith in Christ I do believe
   We shall overcome some day.

4. We shall live in peace,
   We shall live in peace,
   We shall live in peace some day;
   By faith in Christ I do believe
   We shall overcome some day.

5. We shall overcome
   We shall overcome,
   We shall overcome some day,
   By faith in Christ I do believe
   We shall overcome some day.

O

Testimony

261 The answer

Words and Music: G. Arlidge

Dm   Dm7   Dm6   B♭maj7

Dm   Dm7   Dm6   B♭maj7

I   had   lost   my   way;

Dm   Dm7

there was not   a   ray   of hope   Life   was dark; I   could not see an

Dm6   B♭maj7   A7

ans-wer___ Meaning-less and blue.

What was I to do with life? No-where that I looked was there an

Dm   Dm7   Dm6   B♭maj7   A7

ans-wer.___ I tried all the

Dm   E♭   A♭

things that they say___ Give a mean-ing to

E♭   A♭   E♭   A♭

liv - ing.   But the more that I

took them I found   Noth-ing there worth the

giv - ing.   Then I heard of One,   who was God's own Son.
He was cru-ci-fied.   In my place He died.

He had come to earth to be the ans-wer
So He is the One who gives the

ans-wer_ Oh, Lord! what could I do?

I saw that I need-ed You. He for-gave my sin;

poco rit. a tempo

now His life's with-in. And I know the Christ who is the

ans-wer.

262 You need Him too

Words and Music: J.K. Davies and B.J. Heather

I was a sin - ner lone - ly and sad,

Je - sus came to me and He made me glad,

Now He has found me His peace does sur - round me

You need Him too, oh yes;

You need Him too, oh yes; you

need Him too. too.

2. The peace that He gave me was bought on a cross,
   He brought me salvation from suffering and loss
   He died to save me, His own life He gave me
   You need Him too, oh yes; you need Him too, oh yes;
   You need Him too.

3. He gives me power to overcome sin,
   He gives me His peace and victory within,
   My Saviour protects me, His purpose directs me
   You need Him too, oh yes; you need Him too, oh yes;
   You need Him too.

263 If you ask me

Words and Music: N.L. Warren

If you ask me, how I know that Je - sus Christ is

real,_____ I'll tell you that I trust His Word And

not just what I feel. He came to me, He

lives in me, He fills my heart with love._____ I

know Him as my Liv- ing Friend Who leads me on to

Gm   C7   F   Dm   F   Bb

1 & 2   **3**

heav'n a - - bove.   -bove. Who

Gm   C7   F   F

leads me on to heav'n a - - bove.

Bb   Gm   C7   F

2.   If you ask me, how I know
My sins are all forgiven,
I'll tell you how my Saviour died
To pave my way to Heaven.
    He suffered there in lonely pain,
    Cut off from God for me.
    He took the burden of my guilt,
    He died alone to set me free.

3.   If you ask me, how I know
There's life beyond the grave,
I'll tell you, Jesus rose again,
Victorious to save.
    He came to me, He lives in me,
    He fills my heart with love.
    I know Him as my living Friend
    Who leads me on to Heaven above,
    Who leads me on to Heaven above.

264 Surely goodness and mercy

Words and Music: John W. Peterson and A.B.S.

Smoothly, in a steady tempo

1. A pil - grim was I, and a - wan - d'ring,
In the cold night of sin I did roam,
When Je - sus the kind Shep -herd found me,
And now I am on my way home.

Chorus:

Sure - ly good - ness and mer - cy shall fol - - low

Eb

me All the days, all the days of my

Bb7 Cm Bb7

life; Sure - ly good - ness and

Eb

mer - cy shall fol - - - low me All the

mer - cy shall fol - low me All the

Eb

days, all the days of my life.

D.C.

Bb7   Eb

CODA (after last chorus only)

Slowly

All the days, all the days of my life.

Bb7   Eb

2. He restoreth my soul when I'm weary,
    He giveth me strength day by day;
    He leads me beside the still waters,
    He guards me each step of the way.
        Chorus

3. When I walk thru the dark lonesome valley,
    My Saviour will walk with me there;
    And safely His great hand will lead me
    To the mansions He's gone to prepare.
        Chorus

265 O happy day

Words: P. Doddridge
Music: T.R. Jones

1. O hap-py day! that fixed my choice On Thee, my
2. 'Tis done, the great trans-ac-tion's done! I am my
3. Now rest, my long di-vid-ed heart, Fixed on this
4. High heav'n,that heard the sol-emn vow, That vow re-

Eb   Eb

Sav-iour and my God! Well may this glow-ing heart re-
Lord's and He is mine! He drew me, and I fol-lowed
bliss-ful cen-tre, rest; Nor ev-er from thy Lord de-
newed shall dai-ly hear; Till in life's lat-est hour I

Eb Ab Eb Bb7 Eb

-joice, And tell its rap-tures all a - broad.
on, Charmed to con-fess the voice di - vine.
part, With Him of ev - 'ry good pos-sessed.
bow, And bless in death a bond so dear.

Eb   Ab Eb Bb7 Eb

Chorus:

O hap- py   day,_____   O hap - py   day_____ When Je -sus

Eb   Ab   Eb

washed my sins a - way;_____ He taught me   how_____ to watch and

Bb7 (Bb9 Bb7)   Eb   Ab

Hal- le-luljah!_____

pray,___ And live re- joice - ing ev - 'ry   day;_____   O hap-py

Eb   Eb Bb   F7 Bb   F7   Bb7   Eb

day,___ O hap-py day,___ When Je-sus washed my sins a - way._____

Eb   Ab Eb Bb7 Eb

266 My Lord is real

Words and Music: N.T. Faithfull
arr: D.G. Wilson

2. Trust and believe is what you must do,
And his spirit will come unto you
Guide you in His perfect way
Till He comes again one day.

3. The Lord will judge us when He comes
And we'll stand righteous in the Son
No condemnation now we fear
With Jesus ever near

No condemnation now we fear
With Jesus ever near.

267 For me to live is Christ

Music for
Chorus and Verse:

Words and Music: J. White
arr: N.L. Warren

1. Now once my heart was full of sin and shame
    Till someone told me Jesus came to save,
    When He said 'Come home to me',
    He set my poor heart free
    For me to live is Christ, to die is gain.
    Chorus

2. Now there are things that I still do not know
    But of this one thing I'm completely sure.
    He who called me on that day,
    Washed all my sin away,
    For me to live is Christ, to die is gain.
    Chorus

© J.White 1969. By kind permission.

P

268 I've got a song in my heart

Words and Music: G. McClelland
arr. P. Bye

I've got a song in my heart.___ A mel-o-dy, And it's been

there since my Lord___ set me free, And there's such

peace in my heart___ That I can scarce be-lieve it's

real.___

Joy in my life. _____ I want to tell you There's no

C   Am   Dm   G7

strug - gle, no strife _____ And it was Christ a- bove a -

C   Am   Dm   G7

- lone paid the price, _____ When He died on Cal - va -

C   Am   Dm   G7

-ry. _____

C   F   C

269 My story so sad

Words and Music: A.R. Bell

1. My sto-ry so sad,___ Wand-'rin' down life's emp-ty___ road,___ Hav-ing such a hea-vy load to bear,___ Did-n't know someone was there, Wait-ing for me.___ I'd gone my way,___ Tried to find what hap-pi-ness I could,

C   Am   D7   G   C   Am   D7   G   C   Am   D7   G   C   Am   F   G   C   Am   D7   G   C   Am

A hopeless pathway it seems I've trod____ Did- n't know someone was

D7   G   C   Am   D7   G

Chorus: (after vv. 1 & 2)

there,   Wait-ing for   me.   Man- y   years

C   F   G   F   G

spent my way,   Je-sus wait-ed for   me,   When I   heard   of

C   Am   F   G   C   C7   F   G

new life in   Him,   I found the meaning of   Cal - va - ry.

C   A   D7   G   G+

Verses 2 and 3

2. Now He's mine,_____ Sav-iour and my King,___ Lord of all,___
3. Now I sing_____ of sal - va -tion's plan,___ How it's free,___

C   Am   D7   G7   C   Am

___ My life   my ev - 'ry-thing_____ I'm so   glad,_____
___ And for   ev - er - y-one,_____ Seek Him   now,___

D7   G   C   Am

___ When   I came   to Him,   He   wait - ed,___
___ Je - sus Christ, the Son,   He's   wait - ing,___

D7   G   C   Am

Coda after verse 3.

Fine

wait -ed for   me.(to chos.)   He's wait-ing for   you.
wait-ing for   you.(to coda)

F   G   F   G7   C

Outreach
270 Hustle Bustle

Words and Music: R.G. Wright and K. Lamming

2. Got to keep up with the Jones,
    Things are so important!
    Spending money, getting loans,
    Where d'you think you're going to?

3. What are your priorities?
    Who d'you really want to please?
    Living in this world today,
    People seem to lose their way, Oh!

4. Jesus said 'I am the Way',
    Won't you listen to Him?
    For His words apply today
    Where d'you think you're going to?

5. If you really put Him first,
    Take Him as your Lord and guide,
    He will give you life that's real
    Life that springs afresh inside, Oh!

6. Jesus said 'I am the Way',
    Won't you listen to Him?
    For His words apply today
    Where d'you think you're going to?

271 Time

Words and Music: The Crossbeats

that you've lost.—   2. You've been working ov-er-time.

A7   D   A13   A+   Ped_____*   D

wast - ing your time   You may ev-en think that I'm

D°   Em   A7   D

Wast-ing more time.   As we've come to tell you now,

Dm   Em   A   A#   Bm

Yes we've come to tell you how,   How you can re-

D   G   Gm

-deem the time_____ that you have lost.   Well

Bb   A7   D   F#7

we a-gree   there's a time   for   liv-ing;   But

B   B7   E

can't you see,   now's the time   to   give in?   We

A   A7   D   F#

see the time   and it's go - ing   by each day,   And there'll

B   B7   E

come a time | when it's all | gone a-way. | gone a-way.

A   A7   D   D

3. It was sometime in the past Jesus spent His time,
   When the skies were overcast, paying for your crime
   And we've come to tell you now,
   Yes, we've come to tell you how,
   How you can redeem the time that you have lost.
   Chorus

272 Crazy mixed up generation

Words and Music: The Crossbeats
arr: J. and B. Courtie

Let's face it | friends, | the world | is in— | such a | mess!

E   A   E   B7

Be - fore life | ends, let's start | liv-ing!

E   A   B7

lost, but what's the an-swer? Cra-zy, mixed-up

A   B7   Dm

gen -er - a - tion, there is on-ly one sol-u - tion Je-sus is the

G   C   Am   Dm

great sen-sa-tion! Won't you stop and think, Now you're on the

G   F#m   B7   F#m

Final additional chorus only.

brink? Cra - zy, mixed - up Cra -zy gen -er-a - tion

B7   Dm   G

there is on - ly one sol - u - tion; Je - sus is the

C   Am   Dm

great sen- sa- tion! Won't you stop and think, Now you're on the

G   F#m   B7   F#m

brink?

B7   F#m   B7   E

2. Beats think life's a joke, these long-haired cynics of society;
   They don't do a stroke... but why should they?
   Mum and Dad at home have lost control of their pride and joy;
   Oh, how they moan! What's the answer?
   Chorus

3. Can you be so blind? You can't see the truth about yourself!
   Or don't you mind where you're going?
   Jesus knows it all. He knows your situation now.
   Why do you stall when He's the answer?
   Chorus

273 He waits

Words and Music: The Crossbeats
arr: J. and B. Courtie

He does-n't ask that you should know the great-est things.

G7   C

So come to   Him and don't de - lay.

G7   C   C7

Come to Him as   you   are;   Re-mem-ber He's not   far   a-

F   B7

-way from you,   He's not far a - way   from you.

C   F   C   G7

you.

G7   C   F Fm6 C   C6

2.   Why keep Jesus waiting? Don't you know that He loves you?
And He's the answer to your emptiness, my friend.
He waits continually, so patiently,
Will you say yes? It's worth it in the end!
Chorus

© Sky Sounds. By kind permission.

274 The shores of Galilee

Words and Music: C. Burns
arr. A.H. Ramell

Verses 1, 2 & 5

1. See the snow drift-ing o'er the mea-dows;

Dm   Gm   F A7 Dm

Gen-tle death from the dis-mal grey skies

Gm   C

Q

Sum-mer's gone,　Mother Nat-ure's weeping,

Gm　　　　　　F　A7　Dm

To repeat

And her tears　turn to ice in her eyes.

Gm　　　　　　F　D7　Gm

To continue　Verses 3, 4 & 6

soul.　3. Last night　I dreamed I was in Ga-li-lee.

Gm　　　G　D　Am7　　D

A - lone　I watched for hours that sil - ent sea.

Am7　　　　D　　　Am7　　　D

A fisherman's net of twine was ly-ing in the sand. The one that Si-mon Pe-ter left, to take his Sav-iour's hand. own.

2. Man can run from the cold of winter;
    Build a fire with a handful of coal.
    But the blaze of a thousand pine trees,
    Never melts all the ice in his soul.

4. Last night, I roamed the shores of Galilee
    That net, forgotten there, made sense to me.
    Peter turned his back on all he'd ever known
    To follow one who knew the Way, to make that life his own.

5. When the cold seems to be so endless
    Grows a flower, small and weak but alive.
    Spring is here, and the ice is melting.
    'It is finished! ' cried the Lord as He died.

6. Last night, I roamed the shores of Galilee
    That net, forgotten there, made sense to me.
    Peter turned his back on all he'd ever known
    To follow one who knew the Way, to make that life his own.

275 Long and lonely journey

Words and Music: C. Burns
arr: D.G. Wilson

Lord. Give your life to the Lord. And you'll

F#m7 B7 E C#m F#m7 B7

know how it feels, — To be loved as you

Bm7 C#7 F#m

go. On that glor - ious ev - er-last - ing

Am7 E B7

jour - ney. On that glor - ious, nev - er end-ing road.

C#m F#m7 E B9 E

© C. Burns and D.G. Wilson 1969. By kind permission.

276 Your fancy clothes

Words and Music: G. McClelland
arr: P. Bye

C   Am   Dm   G7   C   Am   Dm   G7

1. Your fan - cy clothes,   the way you wear your hair...

C   Ab7   Fm

You cher - ish those,

C   Ab7

You say you real - ly care___   But when the moth and

Fm   C   Em

rust come, The dirt and the dust come. You'll want to

hide, there won't be an - y - where.

said.

2. You buy a car, you keep it shining bright.
   On your guitar, the label is just right.
   But when the night and fear come,
   And you feel a tear come,
   You'll want a friend, there won't be one in sight.

3. You're smiling now, but round the corner's pain.
   You wonder how, you'll ever laugh again.
   Then you'll remember, slowly,
   The things that I told you
   About my Lord, and all that He has said.

277   Listen to the story

Words and Music: **G. McClelland**
arr: **P. Bye**

Lis-ten to the sto-ry

Of the lit - tle can - dle,   Just a lit - tle sto - ry

but the tale is am - ple   Lets you know what I mean

may-be too what you mean When we talk of liv-ing and of

D   Dm   A   B7

1 & 2   3   4

liv-ing to the full___   way a-round.   sto - - - - -ry.

B7   E7   B7   E7   E7   A

2. Stands the little candle in a darken'd window,
   Tho it has potential by itself it won't glow
   Till a lighted taper gently shines upon it,
   Touches it and passes on the light which it has on it.

3. Now that little candle lights the darken'd window,
   Shines for people outside, glows on people in too
   Just a tiny candle with its little glimmer,
   Yet the light is seen for quite a way around.

4. We are just like candles, someone needs to light us,
   We have the potential, someone needs to guide us:
   Jesus light our darkness, use us for your glory,
   Shining as the candle in the story.

278 We must believe

Words and Music: D. Lowe
arr. N.L. Warren

He is the one on whom we can de - pend, He is our on-ly hope,

G   A   A7   D   D7

world with-out end,———— We must be - lieve.

G   Gm6   D   A7   D

2. Jesus, the perfect one was humble and kind,
    Healing the halt, the lame and the blind -
    Such power could conquer sin, renew the mind,
    'Follow thou me'.
    Chorus.

3. Rich, yet for our sakes he became poor,
    He's our example for evermore.
    God's love in all of us means peace not war,
    'Abide in me'.
    Chorus

4. If we are Christ's, and take the Spirit's sword,
    One day we shall see our blessed Lord,
    What exaltation in that glad reward,
    'Rejoice with me'.
    Chorus

5. Learning to live with Christ on this earth below,
    Finding a purpose the world cannot know,
    Looking to Jesus till our lives o'erflow
    'With charity'.

279 Think again

Words: K. Craddock
Music: Cliff Richard
arr. M.C.T. Strover

If __ ac - cess to hea-ven de - pen- ded on you, On the
num - ber of good deeds you'd done; What a
won - der - ful pic - ture you'd paint of your - self— I'm quite
sure you'd rate sec - ond to none.

Last time — To Coda.

4. It is Christ's blood a- lone that has

pow - er to cleanse From the dire con - se - quen - ces of

sin; And it's on - ly on see - ing that

sin cleans - ing Blood That the Fath - er will say "En - ter

2. But God's not concerned with the things you've achieved,
   Though these things may be many or few;
   There's only one way by which men may reach God,
   And that doesn't mean all men but you.

3. Jesus said I'm the Way and the Truth and the Life,
   No man cometh to God but by Me;
   And that way back to God is to trust in the Blodd
   That was shed for you - at Calvary.

4. It is Christ's Blood alone that has power to cleanse
   From the dire consequences of sin;
   And it's only on seeing that sin cleansing Blood
   That the Father will say 'Enter in'; 'Enter in'.

5. All have sinned and fall short of the glory of God,
   And the Bible has made it quite plain -
   That your righteousnesses are to Him filthy rags
   If you think they'll avail, Think again.

280 Have you ever wished

Words and Music: C. Burns
arr. D.G. Wilson

Have you ev-er wished you knew how to pray?
Do you ev-er won-der why you're a-live?

Have you ev-er wished you knew what to say?
Do you ev-er wish you knew?

I know you do. I've found the an-swer for a

lone-ly emp-ty heart; Take Je-sus in your life and

make an - oth - er start.   Oh,

Gm7   C7   Bb

D C al Fine

peo - ple!   Lis - ten all you peo - ple!

F   Gm7   C7

2   I've found the answer for a lonely empty soul;
      Take Jesus in your life and He will make you whole.
      Of people! Listen all you people!

            Anybody saved can learn how to pray
            Anybody saved can know what to say
            Anybody saved knows why he's alive
            Do you ever wish you knew?
            I know you do.

281 Simply believe

Words and Music: A. Winkworth

The Lord___ is my friend   and on Him___ I de-pend.___ He___

E   C#m   A6   B7

guides us— on our way and for- ev - er with us will stay,— If we

E   C#m   F#m   B7

trust,— trust in Him,— He will lead us ev - 'ry -

E   C#m   F#m   B7

day   He will lead us

E   C#m   F#m7

Interlude

ev - - - er - y day.

B7   E   C#m   A   B7

2.   One thing is required that we trust in our God.
For He died on the tree to set us all free
From the bond of our sin, just simply believe in Him.

3.   Come now to the cross with your faith small and weak,
He will help you to believe if only Him you'll seek.
He will come in to your heart and He'll reign in every part.

4.   The Lord is my friend and on Him I depend.
He guides us on our way and forever with us will stay,
If we trust, trust in Him, He will lead us every day.

R

282 His name is Jesus

Words and Music: D. Drinkall

He's the Sav - iour, the One who cares___ His Name is

F   F7   Bb   C7

Je - sus.   How ev - er great the storm   He will

C7   F   Am   Dm

make the wa - ters calm,   And through the dark-est

Gm   C7   Cb7   Bb

night   Je - sus is the guid- ing light.

C7   Am   Ab7   C7

I find com-fort when I read of the things He's

done for me Yes, I've got a Friend in - deed____

His Name is Je - sus____ His Name is Je - sus.

2. When the road seems hard and long and things keep on going wrong,
   Someone always makes me strong, His Name is Jesus.
   Sometimes on life's restless waves I'm a ship without a sail.
   But my Captain will never fail, His Name is Jesus.
   The joy that He imparts brings a warmness to my heart
   That's far beyond compare to the earthly joys I share!
   While I walk and talk with Him all my battles He will win,
   He helps me in everything, His Name is Jesus, His Name is Jesus.

3. Friends around me, young and old, don't be orphans in the cold,
   Come to One who loves you so, His Name is Jesus.
   Earthly treasures you possess won't give deep down happiness,
   Only One ever will do that, His Name is Jesus.
   This modern world today soon can lead your heart astray,
   There's so much sin and strife creeping into every life.
   Yet there's one sure way you can overcome the Devil's plan.
   Put your faith and trust in One, His Name is Jesus, His Name is Jesus.

283 My friend Joe

Words and Music: G. Arlidge

Joe's my friend and he thought I was mad, And he used to work so hard, in the of-fice near the yard, He was work-ing nine 'til five, Think-ing mon-ey all the time, And now he knows

knows   he   was wrong, And now   he   knows,

knows   he   was wrong, And now   he   knows.

Chorus

Je - sus says "I am the Way, the Truth and the Life   And with

me   will   you   on - ly   find   light".

(After verses 1 & 2)   He
(After verse 3)   He
(After verse 4)   He

died for me; I died with Him and so my life has changed And my
died for Joe; he died with Him and so his life has changed And his
died for you; please die with Him and then your life will change And your

Cm · G7 · Cm · G7

1, 2 & 3

world will nev-er be the same.
world can nev-er be the same.
world will nev-er be the

Bb · F · D7 · G · D7 · G · G7

4

same. And your world will nev-er be the same.

D · Bb · F · C · F · C

2. Joe then thought, "Now I'll work for the poor",
   And he used to give his time to the people who were blind,
   And he was searching for some point to give purpose to his life,
   And now he knows, that's not enough. . . . . .
   Chorus

3. Then one day when his mood was so sad,
   For he'd given up all hope and his footsteps were so slow,
   But then he saw a smiling man who placed a booklet in his hand
   It was the word, word of the Lord. . . . . .
   Chorus

4. Yes, he's changed quite beyond all belief,
   And he likes to work so hard, in the office near the yard,
   And he's found a new life now, thinks the world of the Lord,
   Because he knows, knows what is life.
   Because he knows Christ lives in him. . . . . And now he knows. . . . . .
   Chorus

284 Does His claim ring true

Words and Music: R.G. Wright
arr. D.G. Wilson

Long a - go, when
Said His Fa - - - - -ther

D   F#7

Rome ruled half the earth, Lived a
reigned in heav'n a - bove

G6   Em7   A7   D   Bm

man who came of hum - ble birth. He

G   A7   D

Does His claim ring true?

Fine

D   C   D

2.   Crowds would follow everywhere He went
        And He told them why He had been sent
        To save the world through God's redeeming love
        Does His claim ring true?
          Hear this mighty Jew
          Does His claim ring true?

3.   Was He just a man who'd lost His mind
        Was He just a fraud, yet you will find
        That He healed the sick and cured the blind
        Does His claim ring true?
          Hear Him for He said
          I will rise from the dead.

4.   Was He just a man who'd lost His mind
        Was He just a fraud, yet you will find
        That His Church was born because it knew
        That His claim rings true.

285 Are you going my way

Words and Music: V. Howard and P. Howard
arr. N.L. Warren

Rhythm fairly free

ask them where they're go - ing, Al-ways they'd say we don't know

C#m G#7 C# G#

Our wild oats we've got to sow, Don't ask questions just you keep on

C#m Am Am6

After last verse

go - - - -ing. Now with Je - sus by my side I'm

B7 (sus.4) B7 E A6 E

on the oth - er high - - - way,

A E A6 E

Now I call to | all my friends, | Are you go-ing | my___

way?___ — | Are___ | you | go - -

- -ing | my | way?___ —

2. So I journeyed down the road,
   The only one I'm knowing,
   Soon my burdens and my cares
   On me began a-showing,
   In despair to God I cried,
   Please hear what I am saying,
   Can't you show me some way out,
   Though I haven't any doubt
   I just didn't know what I was saying.

3. Then one day I saw a man,
   On another highway,
   Called to me across the stream,
   Are you going my way?
   I said thanks I don't think so,
   Why should I change direction,
   He said listen change your mind,
   Can't you see that corner's blind
   Please don't wait too long
   Before correction.

4. I said Okay, what's your name,
   He told me it was Jesus,
   Told me that the road I'm on
   The devil made to keep us,
   Reaching out across the stream
   He said you'll have to trust me,
   As I reached His outstretched hand
   I suddenly could understand
   This could be no ordinary man.

   Now with Jesus by my side,
   I'm on the other highway,
   Now I call to all my friends,
   Are you going my way.
   Are you going my way.

286 Reflections

Words: K. Craddock
Music: Cliff Richard
arr. M.C.T. Strover

One night I had a dream, through a swirling fog I walked a-lone by the edge of a stream I heard somebody groan, I stopped and looked in-to a pool and saw the re-flec-tion of a fool. and

F♯ Bm A G F♯

saw the re-flec-tion of a fool.

Bm A G F♯ Bm

Dragging him by the throat were the

G♯m Bm

col-lar and the links of a chain on his shoul-ders a coat,— on his

A

scared of death, my days just one long fu-til-i-ty___

___ see-ing my emp-ti-ness I

cried "God make me free!" I looked once more and I

don't know how I saw the re-flec-tion changing now, I

saw the re-flec-tion, chang-ing now. A

Bm   A   G   F#7

Slower

man was in my place, a man with holes in his hands and side, A

Bm

man I could not face,— the man I had cru-ci-fied,— on

A

him was my coat, my chains and my shoes, and be-

G   F#

OUTREACH

287 A boy once sat

Words and Music: G. McClelland
arr: P. Bye

Intro:

Cm   Bb   Ab   G7   Cm   Bb   Ab   G7

A boy once sat by the side of a riv-er   Dip-ping his feet in the

Cm   Fm   Cm   Eb

cool, cool, wa-ter, He watched the lit-tle fish-es a - laz- il-y swim-ming

G7   Cm   Fm   G7

by._____   He looked up in - to the

Cm   Bb   Ab   G7   Cm

He'd

Ab   G7   Cm   Bb   Cm   Bb   Cm

(Vocal part vv 2 & 3)

heard a-bout a book and they called it the Bi-ble, and some folks said it was

on - ly a fa-ble, But no-one else could tell him how to

live or what would hap - pen when he died. So he

read, at the start ev - 'ry - thing had been per - fect, But

chan - ges had come through a man's dis - o - bed - ience, But

God still loved him so He sent His Son to suf - fer and

die. And he mar-velled at a God who loved the

birds and the fish-es And yet sent His on - ly lov - ing

Son to suf-fer and to die.___ What could he do now to

gain God's af - fec - tion?___ How could his life___ take a

brand new di - rec - tion? He won-dered in his heart just ex -

- act - ly where the ans -wer did___ lie.___ So he

got down on his knees and he asked for for - giv-ness___ And

when he'd con - fessed, well, he want - ed to wit - ness He

shout-ed to the fish-es in the stream and the bird-ies in the sky___

___ And Christ was the ans-wer to the who, and the where and the

what, and the how, and the ans-wer___ to the why.___

288 The Bible tells me so

Words and Music: Traditional
arr: D.G. Wilson

1. There's a time to reap, a time to sow, That
2. There's a time to laugh, a time to cry, A

seeds plan-ted ev - 'ry day will grow, And oh,——
time to live and a time to die, I know;

did - n't you know, The Bi - ble tells me

so.   3. The good Lord watch-es ov - er ev - 'ry - one,

Ev - 'ry day and night. He made the sun and He

F   F7   Bbm6

made the moon so the fu - ture would be bright.

D.C. al Fine

G7   C7

4.   There's a time to reap, a time to sow,
      A time to pray when the evening lights
      Are low, didn't you know,
      The Bible tells me so.

289   Think of tomorrow

Words and Music: C. Burns
arr. A.H. Ramell

CHORUS

Think of to-mor-row, what will it bring you? How can you face it

Bb   Eb   F   Bb

all a - lone? Though ev- 'ry-thing seems fine To-

Cm7   F   Bb   Cm7

-mor-row is a long, long, time.

Cm7   F   Bb

VERSE

1. The Lord said There is no man or wo-man

Bb   Eb   Bb

That can-not find a place in His love

Eb   Bb

And there is no sin that's big-ger than His mer - cy

Dm   Ebmaj.7   Cm7

(v. 2 ♪♪)

So there's a place for you in heav'n a - bove.

Bb   F7   Bb   Cm7

2. Whoever hears His knock upon their heart's door
   However faint that knocking might be
   You can be sure His arms will be wide open
   And there's a place for you and a place for me.
   Chorus

290 Do you know about my Saviour

Words and Music: D. Lowe
arr. N.L. Warren

Do you know a-bout Je-sus born in sta-ble bare? Do you know a-bout Je-sus com-ing down His love to share? Do you know a-bout Je-sus____ or don't you real-ly care? Do you know a-bout my Lord?

Do you know about my Saviour who died on Calvary?
Do you know about my Saviour hanging there in agony?
Do you know about my Saviour who loves you and me?
Do you know about my Lord?

Now today we hear a lot about the atom bomb and things,
Have you any time to think about the peace that Jesus brings?
Do you listen to the Christian who of his Saviour sings?
Do you know about my Lord?

291 Tell me the way

Words and Music: R.T. Bewes
arr. M.C.T. Strover

We're in a great race to put rock-ets in space, But the needs of our souls we're re - fus - ing to face; I search my - self through for a pur-pose that's true, For life   is   one fran - tic   chase._____

A   8ve
                     E7   A

Some -   one   tell   me   the   way_____   I'm

A   E7

lost   and   need-ing to   know;_____   the

E7   A

tang - les   of   doubt and what   life   is   a - bout;   What

D   A

an - swer   can   an - y - one   show?_____

2. There are Minis and Jags and plenty of fags,
   And money comes easy without many snags,
   Position to win, with a pension thrown in,
   But life is empty, and drags.
   Chorus

3. As a kid I was given one free day in seven,
   With bangers for breakfast and church at eleven;
   Now a garden I weed, Sunday scandal I read,
   Clean car, but no thought of Heaven.
   Chorus

4. To conform is the way in the world of today,
   A world of sick humour and moral decay;
   Love's easy and free, the experts agree,
   But life is swinging away.
   Chorus

5. If God could just dwell on earth for a spell,
   A God who could save from the boredom of hell;
   And if pain could be shared by a Saviour who cared,
   Then why does nobody tell?
   Chorus

Songs and Spirituals
292 My soul is a witness for my Lord

Words and Music: Traditional
arr. O. J. Thomas

put him right down in the li - ons' den! God sent His an-gels the

Bb   D7   Gm   Eb   F7   Bb   Gm   D7   Gm

Slowly

li - ons for to keep, An' Dan-iel lay down an' went to sleep!

Eb   Dm   F7   Bb7   Eb   Ebm6   Bb

Now Dan-iel was a wit - ness for my Lord, now Dan-iel was a wit - ness

Eb   Bb   Gm   D7   Eb   Bb   Bbm

Refrain: after v. 3 only

for my Lord. O my soul is a wit - ness for my Lord, My

C7   F7   Bb   Bb   Eb   Bb   Eb   D7

T

soul is a wit-ness for my Lord.

Cm   Eb Bb C7   F7

Bb

© in this arrangement only, Owen Thomas 1969. By kind permission.

293 My Lord what a morning

Words and Music: Traditiona
arr. O. J. Thomas

Slowly
Refrain:

My Lord,   what a morn-ing, My Lord   what a

Eb   Bb9 Eb   Bb   Eb

Without Piano: (D)   (A7) (D)   (A)   (D)

morn-ing, My— Lord,   what a morn-ing, When   the

Bb   Eb   Fm   Eb   Ab Abm

(A)   (D)   (Em) (D)   (G)

2. You'll hear the sinners moan
    To wake the nations underground
    Looking to my Lord's right hand,
    When the stars begin to fall.

3. You'll hear the Christians shout
    To wake the nations underground
    Looking to my Lord's right hand,
    When the stars begin to fall.

294 Early in the morning

Words and Music: Traditional
arr. D.G. Wilson

Well, ear-ly in the morning   A-bout the break of

D7   G   C6   G   D7

day   I asked the Lord_____ to find the

G   C6   G   Bm

way:____   Help me find the   way

Am7   D7   G   C6

to the pro -mised land   This lone - ly

G   D7   G   C6   G   D7

bo- dy　　　needs a help - ing | hand.　　　　　I asked the

Em　　　　　A7　　　D7

Lord　　　Won't you help me | please　　　Help me find the

G　　　　　　Bm　　　Am7　　　D7

last verse

way.

G　C6　G　C6　G　C6　G

A two-part version can be sung as follows:-　　　　etc.

2.　When the new day's a-come
　　On my bed in prayer
　　I pray, O Lord, won't you lead me there:
　　Won't you guide me safe to the golden strand
　　Won't you lead this body, this burden share?
　　I asked the Lord...

3.　When the judgment comes
　　And the world's in chains
　　And the trumpet blows, won't you call my name?
　　When the thunder rolls, when the heaven's break
　　And the sunshine's fire ne'er shines again,
　　I asked the Lord...

295 Let my people go

Words: E.J. Bash
Tune: Traditional
arr. D.G. Wilson

pull.
go.
It's } work all day with nothing for your pay; And
Who

Cm   Gm Ab Eb Fm7   Bb7(add 6)

bur-y the lo - ser a - long the way, { And pull you He - brews
                                         O let my peo - ple

Eb   Fm9   Eb   Ab7 Bb7 Cm   Fm6 G7

pull,   and sweat,   and die.
go,   from death   and hell!

Ab   Cm   Fm7   G+   Cm

2. Then Moses came and he said, 'Let be!
   The Hebrew people ought to be free.'
   So he killed a man to start a war,
   But the Hebrews said, 'We want no more!'
   Chorus

3. So Pharoah called for Moses' blood
   Had Hebrews gather straw for their mud.
   And Moses fled to the wilderness,
   'I'll wash my hands of the whole blamed mess.'
   Chorus

4. And God in the wilderness Moses groomed,
   Then spoke from a burning bush not consumed.
   'You go to Egypt, fear not Pharoah,
   And tell him to let my people go.'
   Chorus.

5. And Moses came with his fearful rod,
   And Egypt felt the wrath of God.
   In locusts and frogs and lice and blight,
   And first born sons dying all in the night.
   Chorus

6. Then Pharoah rose in his grief and pain,
   And cleared the Hebrews from his domain.
   The Hebrews crossed the wild sea tame,
   And claimed their freedom in God's name.
   Chorus.

296 Didn't my Lord deliver Daniel

Words and Music: Tradition
arr. O.J. Thomas

With vigour

Did-n't | my Lord de-liv-er | Dan — iel, de-liv-er

Gm

Dan — — — iel, de-liv-er | Dan — — — iel, | Did-n't

Cm   Gm

my Lord de-liv-er | Dan — — — i-el and

Gm7

Last time

why not-a ev-er-y man? | 1.He de-

Cm   Gm   D7   Gm   Gm7

-liv - ered Dan - iel from the li - on's den,

Cm   Gm7   Cm

Jo - nah from the bel - ly of the whale   And the

Gm   D7   Gm   Gm7   Gm

He - brew chil-dren from the fie - ry fur-nace, And

Cm   Fm6   Cm   Bb   D7(b9)   Gm   Cm9

CODA

why not - a ev-er-y man. Did-n't man.

Gm7   Db   Cm7   Gm   Gm Cm6 G

    2.   The wind blows east and the wind blows west,
           It blows like the Judgment Day;
           And every soul that's never prayed
           Is glad to a-pray that day!
           Didn't my Lord......
    3.   If the moon run down in a purple stream,
           And the sun forbear to shine,
           And the stars in the heavens all disappear,
           King Jesus shall be mine!
           Didn't my Lord......

297 I got a home in that rock

Words and Music: Traditional
arr. O.J. Thomas

heard my Sav - iour cry, "You got-ta | home in - a that Rock, don't you
died he found a home on high, He had a | home in - a that Rock, don't you

D   G   E7   D   G

see.
see.

died he went to hell. He had no
wa - ter but fire next time. Bet-ter get a

D (G D)   D   Bb7+

home in - a that Rock don't you see!
home in - a that Rock don't you see!

D   A#°   Bm   G   D

298 Come to me

Words and Music: Traditional
arr. O.J. Thomas

1. Come to Me, Ye who are hard op-pressed; Lay your head gent-ly up-on My breast; Come to Me, And I will give you rest, Wear-y one, hith-er come, God is your home!

2. Come to Me! Jesus now gently pleads.
Come to Me! I can supply all needs;
And My way unto green pastures leads,
Free from sin! Enter in! God is your home.

© in this arrangement only, Owen Thomas 1969. By kind permission.

299 We are climbing Jacob's ladder

Words and Music: Traditional
arr. O.J. Thomas

2. Ev'ry rung goes higher 'n' higher
    Ev'ry rung goes higher 'n' higher
    Ev'ry rung goes higher 'n' higher
    Soldier of the Cross.

3. Sinner do you love my Jesus?
    Sinner do you love my Jesus?
    Sinner do you love my Jesus?
    Soldier of the Cross

4. If you love Him, why not serve Him?
    If you love Him, why not serve Him?
    If you love Him, why not serve Him?
    Soldier of the Cross.

5. Faithful prayer will make a soldier
    Faithful prayer will make a soldier
    Faithful prayer will make a soldier
    Soldier of the Cross.

6. We are climbing higher 'n' higher
    We are climbing higher 'n' higher
    We are climbing higher 'n' higher
    Soldier of the Cross.

The first line of a piece is included, in italic type, only where it differs from the title.

FIRST PUBLISHED NOVEMBER 1969

Overseas Agents

EMU Book Agencies Ltd, 511 Kent Street, Sydney, NSW
Australia

CSSM and Crusader Bookroom Society Ltd, 177 Manchester Street
Christchurch, New Zealand

Sunday School Centre Wholesale, Box 3020, Cape Town
South Africa

Standard Book Numbers: 85491 809 4 (Fabric)
85491 810 8 (Boards)

Published as a Falcon Book for the Church Pastoral-Aid Society, 32 Fleet Street, London EC4.
Printed and bound in Great Britain by
Bookprint Limited, Crawley, Sussex

COVER: M G O GRAPHICS